THE DEATH
OF
KINGS

THE DEATH

OF

KINGS

~

A Medical History of the
Kings and Queens of England

CLIFFORD BREWER
T.D., F.R.C.S.

ERRATUM SLIP
Please note that pages
191 & 192 have been
transposed and should be read in
reverse order.

ABSON BOOKS LONDON

This edition published in Great Britain in 2000 by
Abson Books London
5 Sidney Square, London, E1 2EY, England

First privately published as *A Medical History of the Kings and Queens of England*

© Clifford Brewer, 2000

Typeset in Minion by
Geoff Green Book Design
Printed in Malta by
Gutenberg Press

Clifford Brewer asserts the moral right to be identified as the author of this work

A CIP catalogue record for this book is available from the British Library.

ISBN 0 902920 99 5

Contents

❦

Foreword to the Privately Printed Edition

❧

I N R E A D I N G Clifford Brewer's fascinating catalogue of the ill-nesses and the causes of death of the English monarchs from William the Conqueror to William IV, the reader must bear two important considerations in mind: first, that accurate diagnosis of most illnesses was largely impossible until the turn of the century; and secondly, that information of the precise cause of death may, even today, be impossible without a detailed necropsy. Moreover, many necropsies undertaken a century or two ago must often, in the absence of our present-day medical knowledge, have failed to establish an accurate cause of death.

The author of this book, a senior and highly experienced retired surgeon, has better qualifications than most of us to assess the medical history records of our monarchs. It is clear that he has read widely on his subject and has not been discouraged by the paucity of some sources or the veritable abundance of confusing material available in others. There are two monarchs about whom modern knowledge and research has allowed a complete reorientation and clarification of their life and character. The first of these is George III, on whose case the remarkable and quite recent research of Ida MacAlpine and Richard Hunter (*George III and the Mad Business*) has thrown completely new light on his life and time. George III was certainly a wise and kindly monarch who, but for his previous-ly unknown inheritance of porphyria, an inborn error of metabo-lism, would have been far more generously treated by historians. Lord North has much to answer for in regard to the American War of Independence, but it is clear from George III's recorded words when he received John Adams, America's first envoy to the Court of St James's that he had an enlightened and kindly attitude towards his former subjects (see page 355, *George III and the Mad Business*). Porphyria, as the reader will learn, also affected other royals to a lesser degree.

Queen Anne is the second monarch whose medical history has been greatly clarified by very recent research. The stillbirth and neonatal death of so many of her 17 offspring, unique in the history of royal obstetrics, as well as her joint and skin problems, can be explained by the diagnosis of disseminated lupus erythematosus, as suggested by H. E. Emson in 1992.

This is a book to be read from beginning to end in small doses. The inevitably shaky nature of some of the source material means that there must be unavoidable errors in certain parts of such a work. Nevertheless, the numerous large-volume histories of England could be improved by including many of Clifford Brewer's hypotheses and conclusions.

Sir Reginald Murley,

K.B.E., T.D., F.R.C.S.

Past President of the Royal College of Surgeons of England

The King Is Dead, Long Live the King

Nowadays, the proclamation of a new monarch follows immediately upon the death of the predecessor so that there should be no difficulty as to who inherits the crown. This happy state of affairs has not always been the case and, in the past, the death of a monarch might well have created a time of civil strife. Therefore the death was best announced after care had been taken that the new monarch would be fully recognised. For example, when Edward VI died and efforts were made to place Lady Jane Grey on the throne, the news of the King's death was suppressed for some time so that his sister, Mary, might not hear of it.

Although the deathbed of a monarch was attended by many, few were really interested in the dying monarch whose power was about to cease, and all eyes were turned on the successor. Some kings took so long to die that their attendants grew impatient, and indeed Charles II apologised for taking so long to depart. As interest in the dying monarch faded, so did any study of the medical causes for the death, and sometimes little is noted in the records. The burial of the monarch might be a very grand affair or it might be completed after dark (since all funerals took place after sunset), with the disposal of the body itself being of little consequence, as in the case of James I.

However, the interesting consideration as to what was the true medical cause of the death of a monarch has received very little attention. We often have lengthy details of their last illnesses, but consideration of the cause of death, in the light of more recent medical knowledge, has received scant attention.

My interest in this matter was first stimulated by a chance remark from my assistant surgeon. He had recently joined a society

called the James IVth Society. This is a Scottish foundation to commemorate the Scottish King, who had a great interest in all things
medical. James was the brother-in-law of Henry VIII and was killed
at the battle of Flodden. My friend remarked that although much
has been written regarding James, it would appear that nobody
knows what became of his body after the battle, and that he has no
known tomb. Is it really possible for the body of a king to be lost? It
would seem so, and we find that the bodies of several kings have
indeed been temporarily 'lost'.

A consideration of the history of James IV of Scotland does,
however, tell us of his final fate. The Battle of Flodden was an unexpected defeat; the Scots have a history of battles that were either
great victories or tragic defeats. At the time of the battle, Henry VIII
was away in France, having taken the great part of his best troops
with him. He left the Earl of Surrey to protect England under the
rule of his wife, Catherine of Aragon. James IV invaded to keep his
promise that he would attack England if his old ally, France, were
attacked. Initially, he had several small successes and took some
border castles. The last one taken admitted him with little resistance and, indeed, entertained him and his troops well, perhaps too
well. Awaiting the arrival of the English army, they were trapped by
the Earl of Surrey on the southern bank of the Tweed, the wrong
side of the river.

Before the battle, James had warning that all might not go well,
so he arranged that several persons in the battle should be kitted
out as if they were the King, thus reducing the pressure on him. In
all, there were five knights simulating him on the battlefield. What
happened is well known, the Scots leaving their point of advantage
and the left wing under Hulme leaving the field, their opponents
beaten. Stanley then took a force round the back of the Scots and
eventually defeated and slaughtered the Scots army. James himself
was killed and left on the battlefield.

To recognise the dead King and to be sure that he was dead, Lord
Dacre was told to look at the bodies and to confirm which one was
the King. He knew James well and had recently seen him. Dacre
went to identify the body of the King, but one difficulty was that
James had taken off an iron belt which he usually wore. He had
been involved in the death of his own father in battle and he wore
this iron belt as a penance. At Flodden, he seems to have removed

the belt as no body was found with it. However, Dacre was sure that he recognised the dead King, and Surrey accordingly had the body wrapped in lead for carriage back to England. Surrey wanted to be able to present the dead King to Henry VIII on his return from France. He wrote to Henry concerning the body, but got no reply, so Surrey was left with the unwanted corpse.

We can trace the further history of the body by consulting Stow, *Survey of London* (1598). It seems that Surrey left the body, enclosed in its lead coffin, in the attic of the Monastery of Shene. At the time of the Dissolution, this was taken over by the Duke of Suffolk and the body was left in the rubble of the attic. During the reign of Elizabeth, a master glazier, Launcelot Young, who was employed at Shene, came upon the lead coffin. Needing the lead, he discarded the body, although he kept the head in a small lead cover. He took this back with him to his home in London and kept it there for some time. Eventually he repented of his actions and took the head to the vicar of the Church of St Michael, in Wood Street. The vicar offered to place the head in the charnel house of the church, and there it was laid. So finally James came to rest. The church in Wood Street is no more.

The description of the Church of St Michael by Stow reads:

There is also, but without any outward monument, the head of James, the fourth King of Scots of that name, slain at Flodden Field, and buried here by this occasion; after the battle the body of the said King being found, was enclosed in lead, and conveyed to London, and so to the monastery of Shene, Surrey, where it remained for a time, in what order I do not know certain; but since the dissolution of that house, in the reign of Edward VI, Henry Grey, Duke of Suffolk, being lodged, and keeping house there, I have been shown the same body so lapped in lead, close to the head and body, thrown into a waste room amongst the old timber, lead and other rubble. Since the which time workmen there, for their foolish pleasure, hewed off his head; and Launcelot Young, master glazier to her Majesty, feeling a sweet savour to come from thence, and seeing the same dried from all moisture, and yet the form remaining, with the hair on the head, and beard red, brought it to London to his house in Wood Street where for a time he kept it for the sweetness, but in the end caused the sexton to that church to bury it amongst other bones taken out of the charnel.

The fate of the Scottish King led me to consider that of the English kings and queens. It is possible to find out considerable detail from the time of the reigns of Edward the Confessor and William I, and since English history in effect dates from that period, I have chosen the Battle of Hastings and the events immediately surrounding it as the starting point for my observations. Before that date, not only is it difficult to find out the cause of death, but even the disposal of a king's body is in doubt. A consideration of the well-known King Canute serves as an example: Canute died on 12 November 1035 at Shaftesbury, and his body was brought to Winchester for burial. We are told that when excavations were taking place at Shaftesbury in 1951, a glass bowl was found which was thought to contain the heart of Canute. The King had been buried at Winchester in the old minster; exactly where is not known. The old minster was demolished in 1093–4, so he must have been moved at that time. To trace the body thereafter, a brief explanation of the changes brought about by the cult surrounding St Swithin is needed. The Winchester saint had originally been buried outside the old minster, but the great cult which grew up around him caused him to be moved into the church in 971, and placed on a raised altar. Around this altar, the graves of four 'prestigious persons' were placed, and it seems that Canute was one of these. When the old minster was demolished these graves were left in a memorial court, which by the twelfth century had fallen into disrepair. The various remains were then placed in the new cathedral around a raised platform, which was later replaced by a screen. It is thought that on this screen statues were placed of those who were buried beneath, and one of these was Canute. Finally, the remains were placed in mortuary chests, which may still be seen in the cathedral at Winchester.

All these chests date from 1520, apart from two which date from 1661. One of the latter chests bears an inscription to say that it contains the remains of Canute. The chests have been opened from time to time and are known to contain a jumble of bones. The Puritans smashed some of the chests in 1642 and scattered the bones. Although they were gathered together and returned to the chests, it is impossible to say which were the bones of Canute. This one example should give some idea of the difficulty in tracing records before the time of Edward the Confessor.

The lack of care taken with the bodies of kings in Christian countries contrasts markedly with the care taken by ancient civilisations such as Egypt. With a strong belief in the resurrection of the body, people took great care with mummification to see that the body was preserved. The inspiration for this came from the history of the god Osiris, who represented the forces of good, and his brother Seth, who represented all things evil. Seth, hating Osiris, killed him and broke his body into many pieces so that he could not become immortal. But Osiris had a faithful wife, Isis, who searched the world to find all the remains of her husband. These she collected and brought together and the God of Gods, Amun Ra, was so impressed by this act of devotion that he united the pieces of Osiris, who rose again. Thus started the idea of reincarnation and immortality; no doubt the Christian idea also comes from this source.

Why the early Christian kings paid so little attention to their bodies after death is not known. After all, the Christian creed acknowledges the resurrection of the body. In later times, certain kings built some of the finest memorial churches in existence to hold their tombs, whilst others were buried under a plain stone. One of the greatest of memorial churches is Westminster Abbey, founded by Edward the Confessor, so it is with him that we had better begin.

The Historical Pattern of Disease

$\sim$

WHEN WE consider the possible cause of death of persons from an historical point of view, it is essential to remember that diseases common today are very different from those common in the past. The reverse also applies and diseases which existed many years ago are rare, or completely eliminated, today.

We should also remember that the cellular structure of life was not understood until the microscope came into use in the mid-nineteenth century. Until bacteria were recognised, infection was a mystery and the formation of pus was considered to be an excellent sign: indeed, it was known as 'laudable pus'.

How pregnancy came about and what to do with the new-born child were all mysteries. Indeed, child-bearing was a dangerous condition right up to the middle of the twentieth century. Anaemia was a very common condition, as the iron intake of menstruating females was often deficient, while bearing a child put even greater strain on the blood-forming organs. Mother and child had the greatest possibility of surviving the birth safely where there was little or no interference with the natural process. Interference was the great danger, as it introduced the possibility of infection passing into the mother. Midwives who attended at childbirth knew what they should sensibly do for the mother. They were not, however, aware of the danger of infection, although we have evidence that many appreciated the need for cleanliness. Jane Seymour is a classic case where childbirth was followed by infection, resulting in the death of the mother, while the child was in reasonable health.

New-born babies were also at risk from too much interference. They were wrapped in tight bandaging, so-called 'swaddling clothes', which could severely restrict breathing and was a possible cause of pulmonary complications. Babies were fed on the breast of either the mother or a wet nurse, which was much better than offering any form of fluid which could carry possible infection. In spite of breast-feeding, which remains the best possible way to feed, gastro-enteritis was rife and a frequent cause of child death.

Infectious diseases were common. Smallpox was the scourge of the Middle Ages. Mary I was a victim of this disease, which was eventually eliminated by vaccination. Measles, scarlet fever and diphtheria were often fatal. We find that Edward VI, while suffering from pulmonary tuberculosis, developed measles, a condition which is apt to be associated with pulmonary complications. The two diseases occurred together and resulted in an acute exacerbation of the tuberculosis, causing his death. Today, diphtheria and measles are prevented by immunisation and tuberculosis has been virtually eliminated as a pulmonary disease.

Tuberculosis was an endemic disease in the Middle Ages and right up until quite recently. The organism which causes the disease is found in two forms. One, bovine tuberculosis, is a disease often transmitted through milk and causes a mild infection. Following ingestion it affects the glands of the neck, the abdominal glands and so forth, giving rise to a mild form of disease. It has been eliminated by freeing cattle of tuberculosis and by the pasteurisation of milk; today the disease is very rare. The second type of infection is by a 'human' type of organism and is transmitted by droplet infection. When an infected person coughs, large numbers of the organism are expelled into the air and those who breathe in the organism are in danger of becoming infected. This type of infection was a great scourge in the past. The infection passed from the lungs into other parts of the body and infected the urinary passages, the bones and joints, and even the brain. Certain persons were very prone to this disease and we find that the Tudors suffered greatly, Henry VII, Edward VI and Prince Arthur all dying from the disease.

The endemic infections, ranging from mild to very severe, were of course always present to influence history. Enteritis is so frequently mentioned as a cause of trouble in the terminal illness of medieval kings that it seems to have been almost universal in the serving soldier. However, it is probably blamed as the cause of death when other causes were responsible. Plague, so called because of its severity, included typhus, typhoid and bubonic plague. None of our kings seem to have died from this severe form of infection, although the condition did have a great influence on medieval history. The so-called Black Death of 1347, when the condition was at its height, was an infection which had spread across Europe and then reached England through the port of Weymouth, quickly spreading throughout the country. The disease is transmitted by rats carrying a flea which bites humans. This causes fever, enlargement of the lymphatic glands and subcutaneous bleeding (bruising and blackening of the skin), usually followed by death in some 4 to 12 days. A more severe form also exists where the infection goes to the lungs and causes a type of pneumonia. This can be transmitted by droplet infection and is a particularly nasty form of the disease, with a mortality of almost 100 per cent. A severe epidemic lasted for some four years, with milder recurrent epidemics at later dates. The epidemic of 1347–49 killed almost half of the total population and affected all aspects of life. There was another epidemic of moderate severity in the reign of Charles II. Hygienic measures have now made the disease rare, but there remains the possibility of a return if measures are relaxed.

Venereal disease became more common after the fourteenth century and it is often said that the sailors of Columbus brought it back from America. It started in a severe form in central Europe before it became common in England. Syphilis is transmitted by an organism called a spirochaete, which, as the name implies, is a spiral-shaped organism which enters the body through a small abrasion or crack and is normally transmitted during sexual intercourse. Known as the pox, it became very common in eighteenth-century England. The disease causes a sore, called a chancre, to develop at the site of entry into the body. This is followed by a generalised infection as the organism passes through the body. Fever, rashes and enlarged glands develop. There is then a long period when it is often assumed that the disease has passed off, but in fact the organism is becoming established in various parts of the body. It attacks the main arteries of the body and causes damage to the heart and its valves, and affects the nervous system, causing loss of sensation and unstable gait. The brain may also be damaged, leading to paralysis and dementia.

It is a very variable condition and may be found in mild or severe forms. Treatment traditionally involved the use of arsenic and mercury, and more recently antibiotics. A blood test can be performed to see if the disease is present. In his drawings, William Hogarth depicts eighteenth-century 'quacks', who practised as doctors, specialising in the treatment of venereal disease. The treatments given were not always successful in eliminating the condition, which often persisted in various forms.

There is continued argument as to whether Henry VIII suffered from syphilis. One late manifestation of the disease is the development of ulcers on the legs, which develop on the outside of the leg and are usually painless and not markedly offensive. Henry had an ulcer on one (or possibly both) legs, but this was recurrently painful and very offensive. In his terminal state he suffered from gross swelling of both legs. His ulcer may well have been due to severe varicose veins, or to thrombosis of the deep veins of his legs from injuries received in the joust. We will see that other kings had syphilis and received treatment for the condition, notably William IV.

Cancer of various organs was present in historical times, but was not recognised to any great extent unless it appeared on the surface of the body. Bowel cancer and cancer of the stomach were not recognised as diseases, while breast cancer was recorded from very early times and Livia, wife of the emperor Augustus, died from the disease.

Pulmonary cancer, though, was nowhere near as common as it is today: it became common only with the increase of smoking in the 1930s.

When the body of a monarch was prepared for burial or embalming, the viscera had to be removed. This necessitated opening the abdomen and chest and taking out the stomach, intestines and bowel. The liver, kidneys and bladder might then be inspected and the main vessels of the body examined. The brain might (or might not) be removed and examined. The body was then preserved with spirit and herbal material to give a sweet odour. A lead coffin completely excluded air and so greatly improved preservation. The coffin was placed in a tomb or crypt which might be of considerable size and able to hold many other coffins.

James I was anxious that his mother, Mary, Queen of Scots, should have a tomb equal to that of Elizabeth I, who had ordered her execution. He therefore moved her to Westminster Abbey and built a very large tomb. This was so spacious that several persons were placed in it as time went by: Prince Rupert and his wife, the 16 little coffins of the tiny babies of Queen Anne, and the ten babies of James II. The poor beheaded Queen rests with so many small, innocent children.

Those who prepared a monarch for burial and possible embalming sometimes reported their findings and gave an indication as to the possible cause of death. A limited post-mortem was occasionally performed by a number of doctors. However, since the diagnosis made by the doctors often depended on gross symptoms, it was often far from the truth. Moreover, during the monarch's lifetime protocol prevented the doctors from examining the patient in a clinical sense. In some cases it was so strict that they were not allowed to speak unless spoken to first. This prevented them from making any real enquiry as to the symptoms of disease, so naturally their ideas were somewhat limited. So restricted were they that when Caroline, the wife of George II, was dying of a strangulated umbilical hernia, the doctors did not even know that this existed. They were prevented from examining her and, until the King told them of the condition, were completely unaware of what they were supposed to be treating. Perhaps it is little wonder that the findings at death, when the body is embalmed, were often the first indication that a particular disease was present.

Those who attended on kings had little knowledge of disease and no knowledge of true pathology. They were naturally anxious that they should not be blamed for the outcome of any illness, so it was usual to have a number of medical attendants in order that the responsibility could be shared. If possible, the king himself might be held responsible for the state of affairs, as with John, who 'ate a surfeit of peaches and new cider'. (Obviously no blame was to be attached to his physicians.) Or Edward III, who 'against advice...rode out and contracted a chill', which was naturally the King's fault. Their wish to have no blame attached might be explained by the fate of the Jewish physician who attended to Richard I and who seems to have been killed on the death of the King. Thus the Duke of Buckingham was blamed for the death of Edward VI, since he was responsible for the medical treatment given. The medical attendants relied on safety in numbers and in their 'explanation' of the death to avoid any blame. As they were not aware of the true nature of disease, their treatments today appear to be appalling. The death of Charles II is perhaps the most terrible when we read of all the many and varied forms of treatment he had to endure.

The letting of blood became very popular and was used for almost any form of trouble. While in some circumstances this might have helped, it was much more likely to be a great hindrance to recovery. The bleeding of pregnant women was particularly unfortunate.

Mental disease is always a very difficult condition both to treat and to record. Henry VI had a recurrent mental abnormality about which little is recorded. George III suffered from so severe a mental abnormality for such a very long time that his has been recorded with some considerable detail. It is now felt that his condition had a physical cause and that the abnormality may be traced back to Tudor times.

It is very surprising how many kings seem to have accepted the fact that they were about to die. They took to their beds in a very lucid state, having committed their souls and made suitable arrangements for their succession. The acceptance of death was clearly a feature of medieval times.

The expectation of life being so much shorter than today, diseases of old age were much less common. Blood diseases, anaemia, diabetes, cardiac afflictions and renal abnormality were barely known and are not mentioned when describing the afflictions of royalty, so we have no way of knowing if they were present.

An examination of royal remains has been done in several cases. Usually it takes the form of a very superficial examination prior to the internment. During the reign of Queen Victoria, Westminster Abbey was 'straightened up' and several tombs were examined. Lost kings, such as James I, were found. It seems strange that the body of any king should have become misplaced, but James had indeed been lost and no record could be found of his whereabouts. The fact that he was eventually found in somebody else's tomb is even stranger.

It would be most interesting to examine the body of Henry VIII, as his bones would tell us, at long last, whether he did or did not have syphilis. They might even tell us the cause of his ulcer. Improved methods of examination, such as screening, might be able to give us information without the necessity of disturbing the body to any great extent. In the meantime, speculation does have its own interest.

Edward the Confessor

Born 1019
Died London, 5 January 1066

EDWARD was the son of Ethelred the Unready and Emma of Normandy. He spent the first 25 years of his life in Normandy, then became King following the ferocious Harthacanute, who died at the early age of 25. Harthacanute was at a wedding feast at Lambeth when, 'standing at his drink he suddenly fell to the ground with fearful convulsions and those who were near him caught him, and he spoke no word afterwards.' In the case of such a fit young man, these symptoms seem to point to a case of poisoning with a substance such as strychnine. We will never know if he died a natural or unnatural death, but it was greatly to Edward's advantage. Edward's succession was readily accepted: 'all the people then received Edward as king as was his natural right.' This gives us some indication as to who may have been responsible for Harthacanute's sudden death, and it may bear some relationship to the death, at a later date, of another opponent, Earl Godwin, the father of Harold.

We are apt to think of Edward the Confessor as a very saintly figure but at the time of his kingship many complained of his character. He was said to be 'very slothful, to have an unsteady attention to duty with fits of ill-timed energy and to be devoid of sound judgement'. He had, however, a great zeal for collecting relics. He also gave freely to churches and monasteries and he founded the great abbey of St Peter at Westminster. It was from these acts that he obtained his name.

Edward was crowned at Winchester in April 1043. He married

Editha, the daughter of Earl Godwin, and in the early part of his reign she was a great support. By 1051, however, Edward and Earl Godwin had quarrelled to such an extent that Godwin and his sons were driven from England after having raised an unsuccessful rebellion. He and three of his sons fled to Bruges, while two other sons, Harold and Leofrine, went to Ireland. Now freed of his domineering father-in-law, Edward apparently began to bring Norman knights and clergy into England in such large numbers that they began to provoke resentment. There is no doubt that Edward supported the Norman claim to the English throne, and it is possible that he sent the new Archbishop of Canterbury, Robert, to inform Count William of Normandy of his support. We do not attach sufficient importance to the part played by Edward the Confessor in ensuring that William should succeed to the Crown, for he was certainly biased in favour of the Norman cause.

In 1052 Llewellyn of Wales invaded Herefordshire, while Harold Godwin sailed from Ireland to ravage the south coast. He was joined by his father from Bruges and the two fleets joined forces and sailed into the Thames estuary. Without an actual battle Edward was forced to accept a defeat and Godwin and his sons were restored to power. The many Frenchmen introduced by Edward were dismissed, thus ensuring that William would not have a peaceful succession to the Crown.

However, Earl Godwin did not live long after his triumph over Edward. He died at Winchester in 1053, apparently of a stroke while at dinner with Edward in Winchester. Like Harthacanute, he seems to have died in an instant. Since his son Harold now gained power, the elimination of Earl Godwin did not greatly help Edward.

The King's half-brother, Edmund Ironside, had a son, Edward, who might well have been considered the natural heir to the throne after Edward the Confessor. In 1057 this son was brought to England from Hungary, where he had lived for some 40 years. He came in good health, but was to perish very quickly in England. He never met his uncle, the King, but is said to have died a 'miserable fate' with no official record as to how this was brought about. Thus three rivals to Edward the Confessor had now died in unusual circumstances.

For the last ten years of his life, Edward the Confessor is hardly mentioned in the chronicles. He may well have spent his time in prayer and meditation, as is suggested. His work of building a great church continued, and for some 14 years he spent one-tenth of his income on the church dedicated to St Peter. Thus came about the great foundation which was to house the remains of so many of the later kings. It was consecrated on 18 December 1065, and Edward died a few weeks later, on 5 January 1066.

Edward's funeral was held the following day. This haste was necessary for Harold, who had gone straight from the death chamber to the Witan to be elected to the Crown. He was told, however, that he could not be legally crowned until his predecessor had been buried. By ancient custom, Eldred, Primate of Northumbria, asked the consent of the people and then Harold, the last of the Saxon kings, received the regalia: the crown, the sceptre and cross, and the rod with a dove representing the threefold oath: to preserve peace, enforce justice and maintain mercy.

Seen today, Edward's tomb has become a very plain affair. It has passed through many interesting historical times and his burial influenced that of many kings to follow. Edward was buried with the ring of St John on his finger. The story goes that the saint had given this ring to a beggar for want of alms. Two pilgrims to the Holy Land then received the ring from a figure of St John, who appeared and charged them to take the ring back to paradise in six months' time. This ring remained in Edward's tomb until Henry II removed the body and placed the ring among the abbey's relics. Edward also wore a gold crucifix around his neck.

Edward's tomb was to witness an early miracle. Wulstan, Bishop of Worcester, a Saxon, was summoned to give up his staff and ring by Lanfranc, Primate, who is described as 'a very idiot, unacquainted with the French language'. Wulstan refused, saying (presumably in Saxon) that he had been appointed by his Holy King, Edward, and he appealed to Edward to take away his staff, or leave it with him on his judgement. Walking to Edward's tomb, he thrust the pastoral staff into the stone, where apparently it remained firmly embedded. Gundolf, the Bishop of Rochester, and others were ordered by Lanfranc to pull out the staff but they all failed. The new King, William, was summoned and went with Lanfranc to the tomb, where Wulstan now asked the Confessor to return his staff to him if he thought that it was right. The staff came away into the hands of Wulstan as if it had been stuck in clay. The King and the archbishop knelt and asked his forgiveness, which in the case of William must have been a great effort. Wulstan was to be the only Saxon bishop present at the coronation of William.

So began the reverence of the tomb of Edward the Confessor, to which pilgrimages were made in the following years. Reverence for the tomb grew year by year, but in 1089 there was a dispute concerning the preservation of the body. Some stated that the body would have crumbled away, others that it was incorruptible. The abbot accordingly decided to open the tomb in the presence of a senior ecclesiastic, Gundolf, Bishop of Rochester.

The chronicler Alured of Rievaulx describes the events on opening the sepulchre:

> ...there issued out such aromatic odours as filled the church with their fragrance. In the first place the burial cloths were clean and substantial; next, unfolding his vestments, they found his under habit and ornaments in the same state. They stretched out his arms, bent his fingers and found the whole body sound and flexible; they next examined the flesh, which was firm and pure as crystal, whiter than snow. But when, after a long suspense, none durst venture to touch his face, the Bishop Gondolphus laid his hand upon his forehead cloth and stroking it over the face, drew it over the beard, which was white as frost. Surprised at this he attempted to draw a hair from the beard, but that adhered strictly. For which, being gently reproved by the Abbot, he owned his fault which excess of love occasioned. After this they preserved the grave dressings and clothed him anew, reinterred him.

The care that was taken of the Confessor and the reverence that was shown to his tomb are in marked contrast to that afforded to many subsequent monarchs. However, the body of the Confessor was not to be allowed to lie in peace for long. The abbey at Westminster lapsed into an impoverished state under a certain Abbot Gervase, who was the natural son of King Stephen. Over a period of 14 years, Gervase wasted the wealth and revenues to such an extent that he was finally deprived of his post in 1154. The next abbot, Lawrence, was appointed in 1159. He had to do something to put the financial position of the abbey into better shape. What better than to have the body of a real saint in the abbey, rather than the body of a saintly king? Even Gervase had realised this and had sent to Pope Hadrian IV asking for Edward to be canonised. Hadrian had refused. Abbot Lawrence, however, made a much greater effort, supported by Henry II and Archbishop Becket. He was also friendly with the new Pope, Alexander III. A Bull of Canonisation proceeded and Henry decided to build a new shrine for the Confessor in front of the high altar of the abbey. This was enriched with statues of St John and St Edward in ivory and gold.

At midnight, on 13 October 1163, Edward's body was transferred to the new tomb. It is said that this was done by the King, Becket and the abbot. The body was once again found in the wonderful condition described above. Abbot Lawrence removed the ring of St John from the finger and placed it with the abbey's treasures. He also removed the vestments and made three copes from the burial clothes. In the new shrine, it now became possible for pilgrims to make contact with the saint's coffin, and thus be healed from their diseases.

Later, Henry III greatly admired the new style of Gothic architecture and decided to build a new church in that style. He also began making a new shrine for Edward in the most costly materials of purest gold and jewels. The work began in 1245 and was to continue until the reign of Henry VII in 1504. The work proceeded or halted according to the state of the monarch's finances. On at least two occasions the costly articles had to be pawned to raise money, but the work nevertheless proceeded, and other relics were added to the treasure. A crystal phial of the Holy Blood was presented by the Knights Templar. Henry, in procession, carried this into the church in 1247. Two years later a marble stone, with the supposed impression of the Saviour's foot, was added. (It is interesting to note that when Mohammed ascended into heaven, he did so on horseback, and that the imprint of a hoof is preserved in the Dome of the Rock at Jerusalem.)

Henry III made a point of always attending the annual celebrations of the saint's day. He lost four of his young children and had them buried in the new church near to the Confessor's shrine. One child died at the age of five. She was 'dumb and fit for nothing', but possessed great personal beauty and was a special favourite of the queen, who fell ill from grief at her death. A fine tomb of marble and glass was made for her.

How then has this magnificent tomb become the very plain 'Edward's Shrine' we see today? Possibly various parts were pillaged as time went by, but it was in the reign of Henry VIII, in 1538, that the pedestal was pulled down and the Confessor buried beneath it. In 1554 Mary I had the pedestal re-erected and the saint's coffin was placed within the upper part of the pedestal once again. It is possible to see that some of the slabs are not in their correct position. The next change came about at the coronation of James II. A large amount of scaffolding was erected for the coronation ceremony so that as many as possible could have a view of the occasion. When the scaffolding was pulled down, much of it collapsed. The coffin was broken and the head of the King could now be seen 'firm and whole' and with its jaw full of teeth.

A Mr Henry Keepe writes that he put his hand into the coffin, and in turning the bones over, drew from under the shoulder bones a gold crucifix, richly adorned and enamelled with a gold chain some 24 inches long. Mr Keepe showed this to the archbishop, 'who looked upon them as great pieces of antiquity'. Mr Keepe was then introduced to James II by the Dean of Westminster and he presented the crucifix to the King, 'who was pleased to accept the gift'.

This crucifix was kept by James II and he took it with him in his hurried flight from England in 1688. The Faversham fishermen who took him across to France are said to have pillaged his possessions and they stole the crucifix; it must still lie somewhere. However, before he left England, James II had had Edward's coffin repaired with heavy plates some 2 inches thick. These were bound with iron and the body lies in this coffin today.

Harold

⌁

Born 1038
Killed Battle, 14 October 1066

H AROLD II was the third son of Earl Godwin. As we have seen, he took very little time in having Edward the Confessor buried so he could be crowned King. His reign was to be very brief. He has become known to every schoolchild as 'the King with an arrow in his eye', but the story of his death and burial is not quite as straightforward as is often supposed.

Shortly after his succession, Harold Hardrada, the King of Norway and Denmark, together with his brother, Tostig, invaded the north. Harold hastened north to meet this threat and at the Battle of Stamford Bridge defeated his two enemies. He then had to hurry south to meet the threat of William of Normandy, who came to claim what he considered to be his rightful throne of England.

The consequent Battle of Hastings is depicted in the famous Bayeux Tapestry, but certain features of the battle warrant further thought. Around midday, the Norman archers 'fired high' with devastating effect on the English, and it is agreed that Harold received a wound in the face. A charge of Norman cavalry managed to reach the English standard and capture it, and it is said that these soldiers killed the wounded Harold. The battle, however, continued until sunset, when at last the Normans won the field and the English fled as best they could. The dead were stripped and plundered by the enemy. Two monks from the church at Waltham, which had been founded by the Saxon kings, came to William offering ten gold marks for permission to pay their last duties to their dead benefactor. Permission was given, but they found it impossible to distinguish the body of the dead King among the heaps of corpses. They are then said to have gone to Lady Edith Swaneshals, 'Edith the Swan-necked', a very beautiful girl with whom Harold had been in love. She undertook the search for his body and found the mangled corpse of her lover. It was placed in a coffin by the monks and taken to Battle Bridge and then to Waltham, which was to become an abbey in 1177. Battle Abbey, which was built by William near Hastings, was instructed to pray both for the defeated King Harold and for William, its founder.

In his *History of the Anglo-Saxons*, Palgrave gives this alternative story:

> Years afterwards when the Norman yoke pressed heavily upon the English, and the Battle of Hastings had become a tale of sorrow which old men related by the light of the embers, until warned to silence by the sullen tolling of the curfew. There was a decrepit anchorite who inhabited a cell near the Abbey of St John in Chester. This recluse, deeply scarred and blinded in the right eye, lived in strict penance and seclusion. Henry I once visited the ancient hermit and had a long private discourse with him; on his deathbed he declared to the attendant monks that he was indeed Harold. He had been secretly conveyed from the battle to Dover Castle. He had continued concealed until he expired.

It is known that followers of Harold did go to the field after the battle and it is possible that they might have helped Harold escape if he were still alive when darkness came. The fact that the Saxon army continued to fight until sundown and did not surrender at noon may be of some significance. We will never know.

William I

~

Born Caen, 1027
Died Rouen, 9 September 1087

Some say that his steed, in leaping across a yawning trench, burst the bowels of the rider, because his belly projected over the forepart of his saddle. Afflicted by this mishap he gave his troops the order to fall back, and returned to Rouen took to his bed, his disorder increasing day by day. On his physicians being called they declared after an examination of his urine that his death was inevitable. (William of Malmesbury)

As the King was triumphantly urging his troops to throw fuel on the fire he came too close to the flames and from their heat and the changeable autumn warmth contracted a disease. And the trouble of his illness increased because his horse in leaping a trench burst the bowels of his rider. Much disabled, he hastened back to Rouen, and as his weakness increased during the days following he was compelled to take to his bed. His physicians, on being called after an examination of his urine declared that death was imminent. (from Matthew Paris, *Chronica Maiora*)

WILLIAM I lived a life of almost constant warfare. In later life he put on a great deal of weight and suffered from abdominal distension. By 1087, this complaint had become so marked that it is said that Philip of France jested at his court, asking when 'he expected to lie in'. William was enraged and swore that at his 'churching' (service for women after childbirth) he would come and 'pay a visit to the French King, with 10,000 lances instead of tapers, and all France would see the blaze'. William had an illness which prevented him from any active military engagements for some three months. When he recovered from this attack, he collected together an army and crossed the channel to attack Philip's domains. We have no details of this illness; as it happened so soon before his fatal illness, it might well have contributed to his death. It is, however, obvious that in spite of his great size and recent health problems he was still able to take a very active part in all military affairs. William met the French force and having defeated them he advanced against the town of Mantes, which he took and brutally sacked and burned.

William was born in 1027, the illegitimate son of Duke Robert of Normandy, the so-called Robert the Magnificent, by his mistress, a young woman of Falaise, a certain Harlotte or Arletta. William was a relative of Edward the Confessor, since his father was first cousin to Edward. This may account for the Confessor's support of William's claim to England.

It seems that William was a very attractive, active little boy, and a great favourite of his father. In his *History of the Anglo-Saxons*, Thomas Miller writes: 'When William was only seven years old, his father was seized with a fit of devotion, and resolved to make a pilgrimage, on foot, to Jerusalem, to obtain forgiveness for his sins.' His chiefs and barons rightly argued that such a journey was not free from danger, and that if he chanced to die, they would be left without a ruler. 'By my faith,' answered the duke, 'I will not leave you without a Lord. I have a little bastard who will grow up and be a gallant man, and if it please God, I know he is my son. Receive him then as your Lord, for I make him my heir, and give him from this time forth the whole duchy of Normandy.' The Norman barons did as William ordered and accepted his son as their ruler.

As predicted, Robert did not return from his pilgrimage, and so William became Duke of Normandy at the very early age of seven. He grew into a very energetic and capable ruler, and although civil war ensued, he was victorious. He was often cruel to his enemies and had a very quick temper, quarrelling many times with his family, in particular with his eldest son, Robert. There is nothing in his history to indicate that he was obese until late in life; in fact he appears to have been very healthy and active. An excellent horseman, he personally took part in numerous battles and engagements, including the Battle of Hastings.

Why, then, should William become so distended and appear to be so obese? He might just have put on weight, but the condition appears to have developed in a very short time. This suggests that he was suffering from a mild intermittent intestinal obstruction. It is quite common in obese people, where the large bowel is affected by diverticulitis, an inflammatory condition in localised areas of the bowel which may well cause symptoms of an intermittent obstruction. Cancer of the bowel is another common cause of obstruction, but here the obstruction is usually complete and the condition is associated with loss of weight rather than obesity. Another possibility is that he was having some difficulty in passing urine due to prostatic enlargement, which would have been associated with renal impairment and water retention, giving rise to oedema and apparent increased 'fatness'.

Whatever the cause of his past illness, we know that William was riding through Mantes, which his force was destroying with fire and pillage. We are told that 'his horse reared in fright at a blazing timber and threw its ponderous rider against the iron of his saddle'. William collapsed in violent abdominal pain and the army had to be halted. He had received a severe injury from which he was to die. It seems to have been either to the lower abdomen or to the perineal region (the area between the legs and the buttocks). An abdominal injury could well have damaged his inflamed bowel (or diverticulitis) and resulted in a perforation of the bowel. This is what the chronicles of the time intimate when they say that the fall 'burst the bowels of the rider'. However, such an injury would have resulted in distension, vomiting and severe prostration before bringing death. In fact, William did take some ten days to die after he had received the injury, but he did not display vomiting as a cardinal symptom. Perforated diverticulitis is thus a possible cause for his death, but there is a second and more likely cause.

Injury to the perineum caused by the iron peck of the saddle could injure either the bladder or the urethra, which passes from the bladder through the penis. The back portion of the urethra is easily damaged by a severe blow between the legs, causing it to rupture. In the same way, a distended bladder, which might have resulted from prostatic trouble, can be ruptured by a blow. Both injuries cause the urine to be leaked into the tissues when the person tries to pass water. Usually, a small quantity of bloodstained urine is all that can be passed and we know that the physicians who examined William's urine immediately declared death to be inevitable. They most probably saw the swelling of the leaked urine and the bloodstain. This leaking of urine has severe consequences, as the tissues become necrotic and possibly even gangrenous, increasing the possibility of a severe secondary infection. Without skilful surgical repair the condition is invariably fatal in some 10 to 20 days. The person may remain reasonably conscious until his terminal coma, and this is indeed what happened to William.

Therefore it would appear most likely that William suffered a ruptured urethra. In severe distress he was carried in the August heat out of the stricken town of Mantes. He asked to be taken to Rouen, to the Priory of St Gervais, west of the city, where he could receive the attention of the Order, with its two skilful physicians. They, however, could do nothing. William remained lucid and was able to attend to his affairs while becoming weaker. In increasing distress, it was obvious even to him that he was dying. Finally he passed into terminal renal failure with resultant uraemia and death.

Taking so long to die, William had adequate time to think about what should be done for the Anglo-Norman state which he had created with so much trouble. The writer Ordericus Vitalis gave a plausible account of the dying King, concerned with two matters: his own salvation and the future of his two domains. Of himself he confessed that he had been too fond of war and his life was 'stained with rivers of blood'. He attempted to excuse his actions as self-defence, but admitted: 'I am prey to cruel fears and anxieties when I reflect with what barbarities they were accompanied.' To hope for salvation he directed that his treasure in Rouen should be given to the churches and the poor, while he believed that the numerous monasteries he had built were erected to 'combat demons and sins of the flesh'.

The division of his lands was a more difficult proposition. His eldest son, Robert, had long been in opposition to his rule and had even fought against him. In fact, he was in the French King's armies at the time of William's death. Robert had been granted the succession to the earldom of Normandy and William confirmed this. His second son, Richard, having been killed in a hunting accident in 1075, William left the throne of England to his third son, Rufus. We are told that he gave his son a letter to pass to Archbishop Lanfranc to confirm his succession. Before William was dead, Rufus set off to England to claim his inheritance and to make sure that his position was consolidated before Robert could make a claim. The fourth son, Henry, was given £5,000 in silver from the King's treasure, and he also departed to see that he got his money from the treasury in Winchester. He was far from satisfied with his inheritance, but lost no time in claiming it and did not wait with his dying father. William was determined that his domain should not be divided. Both Rufus and Henry were able later to unify England and Normandy.

William died on Thursday 9 September 1087. It is said that on that day he awoke to hear the bell tolling for prime at 7 a.m. He seems to have been quite rational and composed, saying on his deathbed: 'I commend myself to Mary, the Holy Mother of God, my heavenly mistress, that by her blessing and intercession I may be reconciled to her beloved son our Lord Jesus Christ.' So saying, he died.

His death was followed by a macabre scene. Those about him are said to have feared that lawless forces would immediately be released on his death, and they all departed with great haste to protect their goods. Servants began to plunder the bedchamber, taking all that they could carry: linen, furniture, arms, silver and all vestments. They left the King's body naked on the floor. There was panic in the streets of Rouen.

The Archbishop of Rouen gave orders that the King's body was to be taken to the Monastery of St Stephen in Caen, but nobody remained to prepare the body or to take it away. An obscure person, a Norman gentleman called Herluin, came to the dead King's aid and had his body taken by boat down the Seine to the outskirts of Caen. Here a host of mourners had gathered and they took the body in procession. Unfortunately they were interrupted by a severe fire, and the procession had to scatter to extinguish it while the few remaining took the body into the Church of St Stephen.

An assembly was now formed which included Henry, who had recently returned from England. The Bishop of Lisieux preached a sermon. Forgiveness was asked for the dead King, and offered for any who had suffered at his hands, and the body was about to be lowered into its grave.

At this point, a knight called Ascelin of Caen arose and said that the church had been built by William on land taken by force from his father and that he forbade the burial on ground therefore consecrated after such a happening. Consternation reigned in the church. Ascelin and others were questioned and all upheld that he had been deprived of the land by force. Henry and the bishops who were present held a hurried consultation: Ascelin was to be given 60 shillings for William's grave and promised the full price of his father's estate. He accepted the offer and the bier was carried to the altar, before which lay a large stone coffin.

The swollen state of William's body in his last months would have persisted after death. The lower part of the torso and the legs were particularly affected, and it was found that the coffin was much too small to receive the body of the King. Those who tried to force him in did so with the greatest difficulty, but to add to the horror, the body burst open and filled the church with such a stench of fearful corruption that the service was concluded with great haste. Even in death William was beset with difficulties.

His stone coffin was then enclosed in a splendid shrine built by Rufus in honour of his father. He commissioned the famous goldsmith Otto for the work, who also designed the columns of white marble on which the shrine was raised. It bore an inscription by Thomas, Archbishop of York, and was to survive undisturbed until 1552 when, on the instructions of the Pope, the tomb was opened and the body examined, after which it was reverently reinterred. It appears to have been in a very reasonable state of preservation. In 1562 the Calvinists invaded the church and rifled the tomb, scattering the remains, with the exception of one thighbone. This single relic was preserved and in 1642 it was reburied under a new monument, which in turn was replaced with a more elaborate structure a century later. In the revolutionary riots of 1783 this new monument was demolished. Now, a simple stone slab with a nineteenth-century inscription marks his resting-place.

What has become of the remaining single thighbone is not really known, but local tradition says that it lies buried beneath the present simple slab. Others think that it was destroyed in the riot of 1783. In recent times, much of Caen was destroyed in 1944, in the fighting to liberate William's Normandy. The Church of St Etienne Abbeye aux Hommes escaped damage, so that the single thighbone was able to rest in peace.

A thighbone, which the French authorities declared to be genuine, was discovered in the old tomb and reburied under a new tomb on 9 September 1987.

William II

~

Born Caen, 1060
Died New Forest, 2 August 1100

When a great stag passed before him the King shouted to Walter Tyrel, a knight, 'Shoot damn you'. The shaft flew, and glancing off a tree pierced the King full in the heart, so that he instantly dropped dead. (From Matthew Paris, *Chronica Maiora*)

Thinking to bring down another stag which chanced to pass by, the headstrong and reckless Walter pierced the Royal bosom with a fatal arrow. The smitten King uttered no sound, but breaking off as much of the shaft as stuck out of his body forthwith fell on his wound, and so hastened his death. (William of Malmesbury)

WE ARE ON firm ground when we consider the death of William II, known as William Rufus, since it is certain that he was killed by an arrow (a crossbow bolt), which had struck him full in the chest. William had been missing from his hunting party and when a search was made, his corpse was found with the arrow in place. There are several accounts of his death written shortly after the event, during the reign of Henry I, which of course confirm that the death had been an accident. They even name the person who had shot the fatal arrow.

It was essential for Henry that the death should be accepted as an accident. Hulme, writing shortly after the event, gives the following account of the affair. The King had had an ominous dream the previous night after having drunk heavily, and so was disinclined for the chase. However, he did go out in the afternoon. There were two parties hunting: one with the King, who seems to have hunted with only one attendant, a very unusual situation; the other, a large party who were hunting with Henry. Hulme writes of William, in his *History of England* (1888):

> Walter Tyrrel, a French gentleman, remarkable for his address in archery, attended him in this recreating, of which the New Forest was the scene; and as William had dismounted after a chase, Tyrrel, impatient to show his dexterity, let fly an arrow at a stag which had suddenly started before him. The arrow glanced from a tree, struck the King in the breast, and instantly slew him; while Tyrrel, without informing anyone of the accident, put spurs to this horse, hastened to the seashore, embarked for France and joined a crusade in an expedition to Jerusalem. A penance which he imposed upon himself for his involuntary crime. The body of William was found in the forest by the country people, and was buried without any ceremony in Winchester. His courtiers were negligent in performing their last duties to their master who was little beloved. Everyone was too much occupied in the interesting subject of fixing his successor to attend to the funeral of the dead king.

Such is the generally accepted story of his death. William of Malmesbury, Florence of Worcester and Simon of Durham all wrote within 40 years of William's death, confirming this account. However, Sergerius, the Abbot of St Denis, who was a contemporary and friend of Tyrrel, wrote in L*ife of Louis Le Gros, King of France*: 'He often heard Tyrrel affirm upon oath that he neither came that day into the part of side of the forest where the king hunted, nor ever saw him there.'

It does seem convenient that a very unpopular king was killed while his brother, who aspired to the throne, was hunting in the vicinity. Certainly, the brother, Henry, seems to have been prepared for the hurried dash he had to make to Winchester, leaving his dead brother to be carried there in a collier's cart. He seized the royal treasure at Winchester and had himself proclaimed King on 3 August 1100, the day after the death of William Rufus. On Sunday 5th he was crowned in London by Bishop Maurice. His haste was obviously to secure the crown before his brother Robert, who was on a crusade, could stake a claim.

In order to understand the death of Rufus, we need to study the somewhat unusual relationship which existed between the children of William I. William spent much of his life in conflict with his eldest son Robert, and it was with difficulty that he was persuaded to leave Normandy to him. He left the kingdom of England to Rufus, his third son. The second son, Richard, Duke of Bernay, had been killed by a stag while out hunting. A hunting accident had, therefore, already disposed of one claimant to the throne. However, Robert was a very popular man, so much so that Rufus was not accepted by the Normans in England, in spite of the letter he carried to Bishop Lanfranc giving him the inheritance. Rufus had to fight several minor battles against the Norman barons in England to secure his throne, and he was successful in this only because he had support from the Saxon barons. (It seems strange that it was the English who gave their support to the Norman King.) Having settled the country, Rufus now turned his attention to Normandy where his brother Robert was duke. Robert was an attractive and easy-going person who was very popular and had the support of the French King. He was thus too strong to be displaced.

Meanwhile, his brother Henry had bought Cotentin in France with part of his inheritance, so Robert and Rufus now joined forces to expel him. By treaty, Robert and Rufus agreed that if either died without issue, the other would inherit all his possessions. Henry soon capitulated and went back to England.

Robert was to play a leading part in the first crusade in 1085, which reduced his influence on events in England. Rufus was thus free to reign and this he did, antagonising many factions. With only the grudging support of the Norman barons in England, he now also offended the Church by keeping the see of Canterbury empty for four years after the death of Lanfranc and seizing the revenues. Finally, under pressure from Rome, Rufus was forced to appoint Anselm as archbishop, but he constantly quarrelled with Anselm who eventually left, taking refuge in Rome. The Pope considered excommunicating Rufus. As for his English friends, who had helped Rufus when the Norman element rebelled, they were not rewarded for their efforts on his behalf. Rufus therefore had enemies on all sides: Norman, English and the Church. There were many to profit by his death, but none so greatly as the Church.

If Rufus were to die, however, Henry would be in a difficult position since his two brothers had agreed that on the death of either, the other should inherit. Should Rufus die, Henry would in theory be excluded. It was thus essential that the occasion of Rufus's death should be such as to allow Henry to consolidate his position before Robert could claim the throne. In August 1100, conditions were ideal, as Robert was away on a crusade. And since Rufus was most unpopular, there would be no great trouble if he were to die accidentally.

Looking at all these considerations, there seems to be a very real possibility that Rufus was murdered; that he was shot with an arrow and his body was left, or placed, in a glade of the New Forest, there to be found by local people who brought him to Winchester. Henry, supported by the Church, is the immediate suspect, particularly because preparations to confirm his claim were obviously made with some care before the death. After the event, nobody dared suggest that Rufus had been killed by anything other than an accident.

Rufus was buried in the Cathedral Church of St Swithin in Winchester, with little ceremony as the funeral took place with all haste. Henry was not present, having gone to London for his coronation. Today, there is a grave for Rufus in the centre of the choir of the cathedral, marked with the King's name in a plain tomb. This grave was opened in 1968 and many bones were found in a reasonable state, along with the shaft of an arrow, possibly that which had killed him. The bones were replaced and the tomb resealed.

Around the screen of the cathedral there are a number of mortuary chests containing the bodies of the early kings and bishops of England. They had been taken from the church which predated the cathedral. In the south presbytery aisle, the second such mortuary chest reads: 'In this chest and in the one opposite are the remains of Cnut and Rufus Kings, of Emma Queen and of Wina and Alwyn, Bishops.' It is therefore not quite clear where Rufus lies. We might have a clearer picture if the tomb in the choir was examined by modern forensic methods; perhaps this will be done in the future.

Henry I

⌇

Born July 1068
Died St Denis Le Ferment, 1 December 1135

He ate voraciously of a lamprey, which he was accustomed to delight in more than anything else and paid no attention to his physicians when they forbade it to him. But when his weakness had overcome his natural strength King Henry yielded to fate. (From Matthew Paris, *Chronica Maiora*)

He devoured lampreys, which always disagreed with him, though he was exceedingly fond of them; and when his physicians forbade him eat them the king did not heed their wise advice. This feast then provoked an evil humour (it is an active cause of such things), cooling his aged frame to a fatal degree, set up a sudden and extreme disturbance. His constitution, struggling against this, excited a fever by way of frustrating the attack of the hurtful matter. But since he could withstand it by no means the great King died on the first day of December. (Henry of Huntingdon)

H ENRY was the fourth son of William the Conqueror and is known as 'Beauclerc' from his ability to read and write, an attainment which neither his father nor any of his brothers reached. He reigned for 35 years, which is a very long time for this period of history. He succeeded to the throne of England on the death of Rufus, when he seized power before the rightful son, Robert of Normandy, could come to claim his inheritance. There were many attempts to put Robert on the throne, so six years after he had become King, Henry invaded Normandy and defeated

Robert at the Battle of Tinchebraie. Robert was captured and brought to England, then held as a prisoner for 28 years until his death. He has a very beautiful tomb in Gloucester Cathedral.

Henry was a muscular man with thick black hair. Described as energetic but cruel, he is said to have had a nagging fear that he might be assassinated. He married Matilda, a Scottish princess, by whom he was linked to the old Wessex line of kings. He had numerous illegitimate children, but unfortunately no male heir who lived to succeed him.

Henry's only son was drowned on 25 November 1120. Henry and his family were about to return to England from Harfleur when a certain Thomas Fitzstephen came to him as captain of a ship, the *Blanche Nef.* This ship, under the captaincy of his father, had carried William the Conqueror to England on his historic invasion, and Thomas Fitzstephen asked that he might carry the Conqueror's son to England. Henry had already made arrangements for his own return, but he allowed his son to travel in the ship, along with others of his household. As the ship was very fast, it set sail after Henry had departed. The crew and all who were to sail in her feasted and drank heavily before departing, and most of them were drunk. Leaving the harbour, the ship struck a submerged rock on the port side and was so severely damaged that it immediately capsized. Only two men were able to save themselves by clinging to the wreckage, a butcher and a noble. The butcher was a man named Berold, from Rouen. It was a cold night and he was to remain in the water most of the night, but he wore a sheepskin coat and survived. The nobleman was overcome with the cold and lost his grip on the wreckage and drowned, leaving the butcher to tell the tale. No one dared to tell the King of his loss, but a child was found whose grief conveyed the message. Henry is said to have never smiled again.

Henry was greatly concerned for his succession and took his daughter Matilda to England in order to get the nobles to swear support for her and her children. Matilda married Geoffrey Plantagenet and bore him three sons, Henry, Geoffrey and William. It is said that Henry found great delight in his grandchildren.

On 1 December 1135, Henry was now 67, a great age for this time.

Reasonably fit, he had been out hunting and it was on his return that he ate the fateful dish of lampreys. He immediately became very ill indeed. His physicians, anxious to exonerate themselves from the illness, all said that they had advised against the meal. We read that Henry was very fond of lampreys, a type of eel-like fish with a sucker on the top of its head, by means of which it attaches itself to other fish. It sucks nourishment from its host, and is a very unattractive creature. It was essential to make it quite clear that there was no possibility of poisoning; all accounts say that the meal was the cause of the King's death. There is, therefore, the possibility that the fish were infected: salmonella, or some such organism, might well have been present and in the case of an old person prove fatal. We are told that Henry developed a fever and finally died, so this is one possibility.

However, the rapidity of the onset of his symptoms argues against such an infection, which tends to take some time to develop. All sources agree that the ill-chosen meal was followed by immediate illness. Therefore an acute gastrointestinal condition, such as a peptic perforation, seems to be the most likely cause of what followed. As he had been well before the attack, a duodenal perforation appears more likely than a gastric ulcer. After the perforation a patient develops peritonitis, with fever and vomiting followed by rapid collapse and death. This is what seems to have occurred.

The body of Henry was returned to England. There are no details of him being embalmed and there was no post-mortem examination. His physicians all agreed that the fault lay with the King, who had insisted in eating the meal against their advice. Henry was buried in Reading Abbey. At the time of his death, he was happily on his way to meet his daughter and her children, and it is most unlikely that he had left the kingdom to his nephew Stephen, who was to claim the throne.

Stephen

~

Born 1097
Died Dover, 25 October 1154

I N   S P I T E of the trouble taken by Henry I to see that his daugh-
ter Matilda should succeed him, he was frustrated in his wishes.
At a meeting in Oxford, all present were asked to swear to support
Matilda, and Stephen was one of those who agreed. The son of
William the Conqueror's daughter Adela and her husband
Stephen, Count of Blois, he was in Normandy at the time of
Henry's death. Hearing the news, he hastened to England, where he
was accepted as king by the people of London. Travelling to
Winchester, he seized the royal treasure which was kept in the
cathedral. By the use of this treasure and by allowing considerable
freedom to the nobles he gained support, but Matilda also had her
supporters and there was to be prolonged civil war.

   Stephen was crowned at Westminster Abbey on 26 December
1135, by Corboil, Archbishop of Canterbury. His reign was punctuated by continual civil war and general misrule by the powerful
barons, and it has been described as a 'disaster for the common
people'.

   The civil war dragged on to an inconclusive end. At one time
Stephen was the prisoner of Matilda, but he was exchanged for
Richard of Gloucester, who had been captured by Stephen. First
one side and then the other had the advantage. Finally it was agreed
that Stephen would hold the throne for his lifetime, but the children of Matilda would inherit on his death. The major fighting
stopped, although there was continued strife between rival barons

who had been allowed to build their own castles. The period was one of continual unrest.

There is scant writing about the terminal illness of Stephen; he does not appear to have held a very large court. Our two sources are brief. Richard Baker writes in his *Chronicle*: 'He was suddenly seized with the iliac passion and with an old disease of the emroids.' Gervase of Canterbury records: 'The King was suddenly seized with pain in the iliac region along with an old discharge from haemorrhoids.' The common cause for such pain is appendicitis, which in an acute form leads to the development of an abscess which may well burst into the peritoneal cavity lining the abdomen. This produces a generalised infection and peritonitis. Vomiting and distension follow, with toxaemia and dehydration ultimately leading to death. From the little available evidence it seems that this is what happened to Stephen. At the same time he appears to have had a recurrent attack of haemorrhoids. His queen, Maud, had died in 1151 and had been buried at Faversham in Kent. Stephen was buried beside her.

The Plantagenets

◇

FOR A PERIOD of over 50 years, England was ruled by a man from Anjou, Henry II, and two of his sons: Richard I and John. Henry's claim to the throne came from his mother Matilda, who was the daughter of Henry I. After the death of her first husband, she married Count Geoffrey of Anjou. Her descendants were of a hot temper and, although of very considerable ability, apt to form enemies. They reacted to events in a very unpredictable way, which made it difficult for them to make and keep friends.

Today, the reputation of the Plantagenets is founded on Victorian scholarship which, while supporting Henry II, gave to Richard I a 'lionheart' quality and made him into a folk hero. This has been increased by his association with the stories of Robin Hood and other legends. John has always been regarded as the difficult and possibly wicked brother, a reputation founded more on fable than on fact.

Their fiery temper may be judged by this description of Henry's reaction to those who supported his enemy, the King of Scotland: 'The King flying into his usual temper, flung his cap from his head, pulled off his belt, threw off his cloak and clothes, grabbed the silken coverlet off the couch and sitting as it might be on a dung heap started chewing pieces of straw.'

When his son John broke down in fury at his chancellor, Longchamp: 'His whole person became so changed as to be hardly recognisable. Rage contorted his brow, his burning eyes glittered, bluish spots discoloured the pink of his cheeks.'

The family had a demonic energy and a ferocious ruthlessness which was said to come from their ancestors. An earlier Count of Anjou had returned from a distant land with a strange woman whom he had married. She was beautiful, but very odd and had no friends. She would never stay in church for the consecration of the Host and always left before this was performed. Puzzled by her actions, the count detailed four knights to see that she did not leave the church during the service. When the consecration was about to take place, she tried to leave the church but the knights trod on her skirt and held her in place. As the priest raised the Host above his head, she uttered a scream, wrenched herself free and fled through a window. She was said to be Melusine, daughter of Satan and an evil spirit who could not look upon the Body of Christ. From her body were descended the Plantagenet kings of England, so it is perhaps no strange matter that they had so violent a temper and were so difficult to control. It is said that Henry and his sons were apt to joke about this story.

Henry II

❧

Born 5 March 1133
Died Chinon, 6 July 1189

HENRY II was the son of Matilda and Geoffrey of Anjou. He was a strong-willed and very active young man, red-haired, thickset and full of energy. He appears to have been very fit in his youth. He came to the throne with little trouble following the arrangement made between Matilda and King Stephen. Having the Plantagenet temperament, he had a violent temper. He was a very complex personality, who seemed to like keeping the court guessing. 'When he had made arrangements to leave early he usually came late and vice versa. It seemed to give him pleasure to create difficulties. In some respects he was easygoing and on other occasions he would show outbursts of violent temper.'

Henry's reign was one of continued trouble both at home and abroad. He married Eleanor of Aquitaine, a strong character, and together the two ruled western France as well as England. He had three daughters and four very troublesome sons. To maintain peace and ensure the succession he had his son, Henry, crowned King of England; he became known as the Young King. His second son, Richard, was given Aquitaine, Geoffrey received Brittany while the youngest son, John, was to inherit nothing. John was, however, a firm favourite of his father.

All these arrangements did not establish peace. The sons rebelled against their father and in this had the active support of their mother. Henry turned his attentions elsewhere and installed his mistress, the Fair Rosamund, in Woodstock. It is said that he tried to protect her from Eleanor by building a maze, but that

Eleanor overcame these difficulties and killed Rosamund. At the time of Rosamund's death, however, Eleanor was a prisoner and could not possibly have killed her. By Rosamund, Henry had two sons, one who became Archbishop of York and the other the Earl of Salisbury. Henry's part in the death of Thomas à Becket is well known and this is another occasion when he changed from a friend to an enemy, although this might have been the fault of Becket. His children, legitimate and illegitimate, all seem to have been reasonably healthy.

There is ample evidence that Henry was active and free from any real illness, although he did have some periods of depression and others of almost manic activity. The first sign of any significant illness is noted when Henry met Philip of France to conclude a treaty. At the meeting he is known to have fallen from his horse, although there is no evidence that he sustained any serious injury. Nevertheless, he was greatly depressed at not being able to conclude a more satisfactory treaty. He had at this time other causes for depression, as his wife and his sons were rebelling against him, including his favourite son, John. To add to this, Henry had taken an active part in the crusades and it was now learnt that Jerusalem had been recaptured by Saladin. Being a Plantagenet, Henry suffered from the familial manic-depressive syndrome, and in him the condition seems to have been particularly strong, to such an extent that it now became severe enough to create actual illness. He developed a 'lingering fever' which complicated his acute depression. Loss of appetite, inactivity and increasing age appear to have been complicating factors. He then developed pulmonary complications with his fever and it is possible that he had bronchopneumonia as a terminal condition.

His last illness is not recorded in any great detail so it is impossible to be more certain of the cause of death. Matthew of Westminster writes: 'Henry plunged into the depths of despair, cursing the day on which he was born, ended his life at Chinon on July 6th.' William of Newburg: 'From great sadness he derived a fever and this increasing he ended his life at Chinon some days later.'

Henry was 57 when he died, a great age by the standards of his time. The only relative present at his death was his illegitimate son, Geoffrey. He was buried at Fontevrault in Anjou, France.

Richard I

⌇

Born Oxford, 1157
Died Châlus, 8 April 1199

R ICHARD was 6 feet 5 inches tall, with golden hair, blue eyes and an exceptional personality. He was essentially French, not English, and being the third son had not expected to become King of England. The eldest son of Henry II was William, who died in 1156. The second son, Henry, died in 1183. Henry II had taken the unusual step of having the young Henry crowned King, so as to avoid conflict between the warlike brothers and to ensure the succession. He had also given some of his lands on the continent to his children, but this did not prevent them rebelling against their father. Although given Aquitaine, Richard was to spend almost all his life in France in continental warfare. John was the only brother not to receive any lands, but he expected Richard to pass Aquitaine on to him when he became King of England. This Richard failed to do, causing a feud between the brothers.

After quarrelling with his father, Richard made off to Paris to meet King Philip, who was the great enemy of his father. Richard and Philip became very close friends and it is not quite clear if there was a homosexual relationship between them. Roger of Howden, who was clerk to Henry II, writes: 'Philip so honoured him, that every day they ate at the same table, shared the same dish and at night the bed did not separate them. Between the two of them there grew up so great an affection that King Henry was much alarmed.'

They were to fight together and, along with Leopold of Austria, they led the third crusade. Richard married the beautiful

Berengaria, but they had no issue. He does not appear to have had any illegitimate children either, which might support the possibility of his being homosexual.

Richard's coronation, on 13 August 1189, was followed by a massacre of Jews in London, which in turn led to a general massacre throughout the country; the city of York was particularly affected. Jews had been forbidden to attend the coronation, but some came to watch. A riot broke out, which resulted in the unfortunate massacre. Contrary to the impression given in the novel *Ivanhoe*, Richard was no supporter of the Jews.

Richard was undoubtedly a very courageous fighter and a very good general, but the third crusade, in 1191, was only partially successful and it was after this crusade that he was captured. On returning home, he had the misfortune to be shipwrecked. This was particularly unfortunate because he was forced to land in the territory of Leopold of Austria, whom he had offended. He had also managed to offend the German knights, so he now tried to complete his journey disguised as a pilgrim. Travelling with only one boy and one man he reached Erperg, near Vienna. Here he sent the boy into the village to buy provisions, and on one occasion sent him in to barter with a pair of gloves. The gloves were recognised by an Austrian knight and the boy was forced to reveal where Richard was to be found. The house was surrounded while he slept and he was captured. Leopold of Austria was then forced to deliver Richard to his suzerain, Emperor Henry VI of Germany, whose hatred the English King had also excited. Richard was confined in the castle of Trifel and brought to a mock trial accused of having been privy to the murder of one Conrad; of having imprisoned the Christian King Isaac of Cyprus; and of having insulted the Emperor. Richard defended himself and characteristically asked for trial by combat. He carried the day and was released to house arrest. A ransom was agreed, so great as to severely tax England.

By March 1194, Richard had returned to England. He is unique in that he is the only king of England to be crowned twice. On his return to London it was felt that in view of his imprisonment, he should be crowned anew. Accordingly on 17 April 1198, at Winchester, Hubert, Archbishop of Canterbury, crowned him again.

Richard returned to France immediately afterwards and soon was engaged at war with his one-time friend, Philip. On 13 January 1199, he was besieging the Castle of Châlus in Poitou. Just before the assault was mounted, Richard rode around the walls, wearing no body armour, and protected only by a shield. As he approached the walls he was wounded in the right shoulder by an arrow. This had been shot by one Bertrand de Gourdon, who had obviously been awaiting his chance; when captured he said that Richard had killed his father and his two brothers. At first it was not thought that the wound was of a serious nature, but secondary infections set in, with fatal consequences.

Gervase of Canterbury writes:

The king was fatally wounded in the left shoulder. He was fatally wounded in the right shoulder by an arrow in such a way that the bolt, driven down from the shoulder, reached the neighbourhood of the lung or liver, nor could it be checked by any skill of the physician.

Roger de Hoveded:

Bertram de Gourdon wounded the king in the arm with an incurable thrust. Then the king entrusted himself to the hands of Marchadeus, a physician, who, after trying to get out the javelin, removed only the wood, and the head remained in the flesh. It was only when the bungling rascal cut freely round the kings arm that he succeeded in withdrawing the head, but the king died on April 6th, the eleventh day after he had been wounded.

Matthew Paris in *Chronica Maiora*:

On March 25th, he was wounded by a shaft from Peter Basil, poisoned, as was said, but he made light of the injury. Twelve days later, he took the Castle by a furious onslaught. Now the wound he had received there being badly tendered in the meanwhile and beginning to swell, a kind of blackness mingled with the swelling, discolouring the region of the wound on every side; this began to give the king intense pain. The swelling suddenly coming to his heart on April 6th, a day agreed to Mars, the man devoted to martial deeds, breathed his last at the aforesaid Castele.

So we have it plainly stated that the King was wounded by an arrow or a crossbow bolt. The wound was in the region of the lower neck or shoulder, but there is some confusion as to whether it was on the right or the left side. It is possible that the King neglected what was a minor wound or he may have had unskilled surgery. It appears that the wound became infected and possibly even gangrenous; any infection, particularly one coming from horse manure, could cause gas gangrene. However, it is more likely that the infection was of the more usual type, caused by simple organisms such as streptococci, which can lead to blood poisoning. We may conclude, therefore, that Richard died of septicaemia, following a wound to the shoulder caused by an arrow.

It is recorded that after the King's death the castle was taken by storm and de Gourdon was pardoned, while others were hanged. One source says that on the death of the King his general, Marchadeus, gave an order for de Gourdon to be flayed alive. Other writers tell us that Marchadeus was no general, but in fact the physician who had charge of Richard, and who treated his wound unskilfully, failing to remove the arrowhead. Following the death of Richard it was Marchadeus who was executed. It is possible that Marchadeus is a version of Mordecai and that the 'Bungler' was a Jewish leech (an archaic word for physician).

History has, of course, made Richard a very popular hero, although he did very little for England. His quarrel with his brother, John, who became an unpopular king, was also to his advantage. He is buried at Fontevrault, in the penitent position, at the feet of his father, Henry II. His heart was buried in Rouen Cathedral and the tomb itself is in a very beautiful state of preservation. In 1838, a small statue was discovered in Rouen which contained a small lead box containing a silver box, wherein, apparently, lay the heart of Richard 'reduced to the semblance of a dry, reddish leaf'.

Arthur

~

Born Brittany, 1186
Murdered Rouen, 3 April 1203

O N T H E D E A T H of Richard I, the rightful heir to the English throne was Arthur, the eldest son of Geoffrey, John's elder brother. In his claim to the throne Arthur had the support of Philip of France, who had at one time been so friendly with Richard I. It is likely, however, that Philip was using Arthur as a pawn in his own ambitions and that he did not really give him full support.

Between Arthur and his uncle John, open hostilities broke out and the unfortunate Arthur was captured by John on 31 July 1202. He was imprisoned in the Castle of Falaise and then removed to Rouen. He disappeared in the spring of 1203, it being said that he was murdered by John, his own uncle. Ralph, Abbot of Coggeshall, writer of the Cistercian Monastery Records, tells the story:

> Some of the King's councillors representing how many slaughters and seditions the Bretons committed for their Lord Arthur and maintaining that there would never be quiet so long as that prince lived in a sound state, suggested that he should deprive the Noble youth of his eyes, and so render him incapable of governing. Some wretches were sent to his prison in Falaise to execute this detestable deed; they found Arthur loaded with chains, and were so moved by his tears and prayers that they stayed their bloody hands. The compassion of his guards, and the probability of Hubert de Burgh saved him for this time. Hubert, who was the warden of the castle, took it upon him to suspend the cruelties until the King should be further consulted. This merciful appeal only produced his removal from Falaise to Rouen. On the 3rd of

April 1203, the helpless orphan was startled from his sleep and invited to descend to the foot of the tower, which was washed by the peaceful waters of the Seine. At the portal he found a boat, and in it his uncle, attended by Peter de Mulac, his esquire. The lonely spot, the dark hour, the darker countenance of the Uncle, told the youth that his hour has come. Making a vain and last appeal he threw himself on his knees and begged that at least his life might be spared. But John gave the sign and Arthur was murdered. Some say that Peter de Mulac shrank from the deed and that John seized his nephew by the hair, stabbed him with his own hand and threw his body into the river. Others that de Mulac did the deed and this is possible as he was given the heiress of the barony of Mulgref as a reward.

John crossed to England and claimed the throne with the support of Stephen Langton, Archbishop of Canterbury.

John

⌁

Born 1167
Died Newark-on-Trent, 18 October 1216

J O H N , a brother of Richard I, was the fourth son of Henry II and was thus very unlikely to ever become King. History seems to have always made him the villain, the bad man of the story-books of Robin Hood. He was, however, his father's favourite son. There is no doubt that he was a usurper, as the rightful heir to the throne was his young nephew, Arthur, the son of Geoffrey, John's elder brother. On the death of Richard, John was in Normandy. He immediately seized the royal treasure and dispatched the Archbishop of Canterbury to England to call a great council at Northampton. Here he was proclaimed King, although Arthur had the support of King Philip of France. As described in the previous chapter, the unfortunate Arthur was captured in July 1202 and murdered at Rouen, it is said by John himself. It is this act which seems to have earned John the label of 'the bad king' as the details of the murder spread, arousing great horror and indignation. The accusation that he had murdered his own brother's son gave Philip of France the opportunity to seize John's possessions in France. John attempted to regain these lands by force, but was defeated.

Soon after he seized the throne, he encountered opposition from the Pope and from his barons who united against him. They demanded the restitution of their rights and forced John to sign the Magna Carta at Runnymede. The charter was concerned principally with baronial rights, but also contained a few clauses of more modern democracy. John persuaded the Pope to annul the charter after only a few weeks, but it was to be reissued after John's death

and revised in 1216 and 1225, when it became the law of the land.
There were 63 clauses in the charter which stated that the king was
to rule, but must keep to the laws of the land and could be compelled to do so.

John was a small, dark man of very active disposition with none
of the usual complaints and he appears to have been very free from
illness. After signing the charter, though, he retired to Windsor
Castle and here the chronicles say his behaviour was 'that of a fran-
tic madman for, besides swearing, he gnashed his teeth, rolled his
eyes and gnawed sticks and straws'. In typical behaviour for a
Plantagenet, he sent to France for armed forces and appealed again
to the Pope.

Meanwhile, the barons had planned a great tournament to celebrate at Stamford, but hearing of John's reaction this was postponed. Local wars resulted, and John had to march against
Alexander of Scotland, who supported the insurgents.

The barons offered the throne to Louis, the Dauphin of France,
who landed at Sandwich and occupied London, where many of the
barons lived. John was now collecting his forces in Lincolnshire and
starting to march south. John is said not to have been in normal
health when he decided to cross the Wash at an arm known as the
'Cross Keys', an area of sands which is passable at low tide, but is
always a dangerous crossing. What persuaded John to take this risk
is not clear. It is possible that efforts were being made to kill John,
thus allowing the French to triumph, and that several people had
been bribed to tell him the crossing was reasonable, in the hope
that he would be drowned. It was 12 October 1216 and John and his
army had nearly reached the opposite shore when the turning tide
and the water from the River Welland rose with unexpected suddenness. John and most of the troops got across, but the baggage
train was trapped and lost, 'carriages, horses, treasures and man
being swallowed up in a whirlpool caused by the impetuous ascent
of the tide and the descending current to the Welland' (Matthew
Paris, *Chronica Maiora*).

John continued to the Abbey of Swinshed, where he stopped for
the night. Here he is said to have eaten gluttonously of some peaches or pears, and drunk new cider immoderately. He passed the
night sleeplessly, and in pain; the onset of the attack seems to have
been very sudden and severe. The following day, he attempted to

mount his horse, but was unable to do so, being 'afflicted with fever and burning pain' in Paris's words. He was placed on a horse-litter and conveyed to the Castle of Sleaford. Here he spent another night in pain, before being carried the next day to the Castle of Newark-on-Trent. Here he seems to have received reasonable medical help from the Abbot of Crouton. There is no doubt that his complaint was an acute abdominal condition, associated with severe pain and prostration. On the fourth day of his illness, in spite of the attentions of the abbot, he collapsed and died.

Matthew Paris in his *Chronica Maiora* says:

> He fell into such despondency on account of his possessions having been swallowed up by the waves that being seized by a sharp fever, he began to be seriously ill. But he aggravated this discomfort by disgusting gluttony, for that night by indulging too freely in peaches and copious draughts of new cider he greatly increased his feverishness.

There is obviously an attempt here to blame the unpopular King for his own death, but it is more than likely that he suffered from an acute medical emergency, possibly a perforation of a duodenal or gastric ulcer. Such a perforation creates acute pain and collapse followed by peritonitis, with the course of the illness taking some days to cause death. We know that John took some time to die, since he was able to name his eldest son Henry as king and implore his knights to fealty.

While he was dying, messengers arrived from some of the barons who were dissatisfied with the French Louis, but they were a little too late to be of any help. John asked that his body be committed to St Wulstan. He died on 18 October and was buried in the Cathedral Church of Worcester, of which St Wulstan is the patron saint.

There is one other possibility concerning John's death. After Louis had been accepted by many of the barons as king, the French fought several minor engagements with John and events were coming to a head. From Louis's point of view it was essential that John be defeated, since the barons were becoming disenchanted. John, having collected forces in Lincolnshire, was marching south and was now potentially in a position to collect further forces from the disenchanted barons. The crossing of the Wash, with the River

Welland in flood, offered a possibility. It failed, but almost immediately after this event, a meal of peaches and cider made John seriously ill. Perhaps he was the victim of an inorganic poison, the taste of which would be masked by the cider; there is no detail of a food taster at the meal in question.

John's tomb, in Worcester Cathedral, has St Wulstan and St Oswald on two of its sides. He was obviously a little worried about his passage to heaven because when the tomb was opened during alteration work in 1797, it was found to contain a stone coffin holding a decayed body shrouded in a monk's cowl, worn to act as a passage through purgatory. A sword and scabbard were also present. It is said that the exposure rapidly turned the remains to dust.

Henry III

~

Born Winchester, 1207
Died Westminster, 16 November 1272

H ENRY was the eldest son of King John. John had married twice, first to Alice, by whom he had no issue, and on her death to Isabella, who had been betrothed to a certain Count de la Marche. Isabella had two sons and three daughters by John. After he died she married her previous lover, de la Marche, and had four more sons. With nine children in all, she seems to have been a very healthy person, passing something of her constitution on to her son Henry, who was to reign for a period third only to Victoria and George III.

John died when Henry was only nine years old and Louis of France was still in England claiming the throne. The young Henry had the support of many powerful barons who had become disenchanted with the French attempt to secure the English throne, particularly the Earl of Pembroke. They arranged for the Papal Legate to crown Henry at Gloucester with a simple circle of gold, as the crown had been lost by John. The Magna Carta was confirmed to secure further help and after several engagements, Louis was finally expelled. During Henry's minority, the country was governed by Hubert de Burgh and later by Peter de Roches, Bishop of Winchester.

Henry was a reasonably healthy young man, but he did have the usual Plantagenet temperament. Physically, he was of medium height and thickset, with a narrow forehead and a drooping eyelid. He appears to have been devoid of any ability as a ruler, and was apparently unable even to arrange his own finances. He was deeply religious, to such an extent that when he travelled to meet his brother-in-law, the French King, he insisted on hearing Mass whenever he met with a priest and was so delayed that thereafter Louis banned all priests from Henry's route.

When Henry was 16 he assumed sovereign powers. On 17 May 1220, he was crowned anew, it might possibly be said 'crowned in state' for the first time. Now married to Eleanor of Provence, he came under the influence of Eleanor's many relatives and uncles. His principal advisor became Peter of Savoy, to whom Henry gave large estates. His estate on the Thames included the Savoy Palace; the present Savoy buildings now stand on its site. A French knight, Simon de Montfort, who was married to Henry's sister, was also to have great influence on the reign. De Montfort disapproved of Eleanor's many relatives and their influence on the King. Henry fought very expensive wars in France, Ireland, Wales and Scotland. Consequently the Jews were heavily taxed and when Henry had a son, Edward, it was the presents given at his birth which interested Henry the most. War with France was unsuccessful and the treasury bare. By the Provisions of Oxford, a parliament was established to meet three times a year in order to regulate finance. It also denied land to foreigners, which naturally led to conflict. A civil war broke out and, at the Battle of Lewes, de Montfort was triumphant. Henry was captured along with his two sons and the country was now much better governed.

However, Edward, the eldest son, was to escape by a very simple ruse. He challenged his captors to a horse race; as he had the best steed, he won the race and then just kept going, leaving his captors unable to catch him. He fled to his father's forces and raised an army. Edward was an excellent general and attacked Simon de Montfort, who was awaiting reinforcements at Evesham. A massacre followed in which de Montfort and most of his followers were killed. Henry, who was still captive, had been dressed in ordinary soldier's clothes and placed at the front of de Montfort's force. He managed to avoid being killed only by shouting that he was the King. It is perhaps for this act that de Montfort was refused quarter.

Henry was now back in power. His rule was more settled, for de Montfort's reforms had enlarged the basis of the legislature and prepared the way for the establishment of a permanent parliament.

One of Henry's good qualities was that he was a builder of fine

ecclesiastical edifices. Wells, York and Lincoln were all added to in
his reign. He rebuilt Westminster Abbey as a possible resting place
for his own body, and here he was to be buried.

Henry lived until he was 65, which was good by the standard of the
times. As he aged, he became ever more vague in his general behaviour, but continued with his saintly devotion. He began to be ill
at Bury St Edmunds, where he had an attack which was most probably a mild stroke. This left him unable to pursue any real activity
and he had to take complete rest. With rest, he improved, as is apt to
happen in a mild stroke. He did so to such an extent that he decided
to call a council in the town. When the council was about to be
held, he again felt unwell and decided to return to London in haste.
It seems that the saintly Henry was very anxious to be near to the
tomb of Edward the Confessor.

Holinshed writes:

> The King returning to St Edmunds Shrine began to wax some-
> what craxsie but having a little recovered he called a council there.
> But his sickness again renewed he brake the assembly and with all
> speed hastened to London. His sickness so increased upon him
> that finally he departed this life at Westminster on the 16th day of
> November.

Henry most probably had a recurrent cerebral thrombosis, accompanied by the typical symptoms of a stroke.

Henry was buried at Westminster in the abbey he had rebuilt. His
tomb was placed over the site of Edward the Confessor's original
grave.

Edward I

⁓

Born 27 June 1239
Died Burgh by Sands, 6 July 1307

E DWARD was born the eldest son of Henry III and his wife, Queen Eleanor of Provence, on 27 June 1239. He was to prove a very healthy child who was very attached to his mother and later to his wife. A man so hard in his dealings with other men was very tender towards the women in his life. Edward was to live to a ripe old age, dying in 1307, at Burgh by Sands, and being buried at Westminster. Edward proved to be one of our greatest kings, although in memory we somewhat underestimate him.

He had no childhood illnesses which are reported. He was physically strong, being thin and tall with particularly long, thin legs. Hence he is sometimes called 'Longshanks'. He was an excellent jouster. As a child, Edward's hair was silvery blond, but as he grew older, it darkened and in old age it was to become swan-white. He had a drooping eyelid, as did his father. Strong-willed and with no particular favourites, he was decisive in council, so different from his vacillating father. On occasion he was ruthless and cruel in the execution of his policies, particularly after the Battle of Evesham.

Edward became King in 1272, on the death of his father. He was on a crusade at the time and seems to have been in no haste to claim his throne, for he visited the Pope and accepted a challenge to take part in a combat at Châlons, where a great tournament was to be held. There seems to have been an attempt to kill Edward, but he managed, with his company of a thousand knights, to defeat twice that number of French knights. He himself defeated the Count of Châlons, showing his personal fitness.

Edward was crowned on his return to England. Following his accession a persecution of the Jews followed and they were exiled from England, to return only under Cromwell.

Edward had a way of escaping injury in an almost miraculous manner. As a boy he was playing chess when he suddenly got up and walked away. A large stone then fell from the roof, landing where he had been sitting. Later, at the siege of Acre in 1272, a member of a secret society of assassins managed to get an interview with him on the pretence of having important information. He suddenly attacked Edward with a dagger, wounding him in the arm. Edward kicked the man and seized a stool, with which he managed to knock the man down, but in so doing he was wounded on the forehead. It was feared that the dagger was poisoned and some say that his wife Eleanor sucked the poison out of the wounds. Edward was obviously very worried as he made a hasty will, but with the instant medical attention he received, he had little trouble. On another occasion in Paris, lightning passed over his shoulder and injured two of his attendants. While he was besieging Stirling Castle he rode around the walls unarmed – as Richard I had done at Châlons. A javelin was thrown from the walls and struck the ground between his feet, causing no hurt; a stone from a mangonel brought his horse down, but left him uninjured. In battle, those on either side were frequently struck down, but never Edward.

He is the first king about whom we have documentary evidence that he 'touched' to cure disease, a practice most probably started in England as an imitation of St Louis of France. Edward performed the ritual widely, with no fewer than 600 in 1276 being 'touched', this number rising to over 2,000 in 1305. The very large number of persons who came forward to be 'touched' is an indication of the King's prestige.

At the time of his victory over the Welsh in 1294, it is said that Edward gave his son to the Welsh as Prince of Wales. The boy was given to them as one 'who could speak no English'. This is unlikely to be true, as Edward had an elder son alive at this date, Alfonso. His second child was invested as Prince of Wales and Earl of Chester in 1301 after the death of Alfonso.

Edward was on the way to Scotland with his queen in December 1290 when Eleanor became ill and died near Lincoln. Edward was heartbroken and decided to return with her body to London. At the places where he rested her bier each night, he decided to erect a cross in her memory so that passers-by could pray for her soul. Twelve in all were erected, of which three still remain at Waltham, Geddington and Hardingstone. The cross at Charing Cross is a copy, the original having been destroyed by Cromwell.

Much of Edward's life was spent on active military campaigns. Unlike others who fought to maintain their conquest of France, he concentrated on uniting England with Scotland and Wales. In 1276 he began a campaign in earnest, after a quarrel with Llewellyn, the King of Wales. Llewellyn had a brother David, who with the Meredith family supported Edward against the Welsh. Following the construction of Rhuddlan and Flint Castles, the English were able to blockade the Welsh coast and Llewellyn was forced to a harsh truce. The Welsh rose again and were at first successful. However, at Builth, in December 1282, Llewellyn was surprised and forced to fight with a knight, Adam Frankton, who killed him. His head was displayed on London Bridge. The false brother, David, then tried to betray Edward. He was captured and was the first person to be hanged, drawn and quartered for treason: he was hanged for murdering the knights of Harwarden Castle; his bowels were burnt because he had committed his crime on Palm Sunday; and he was quartered for rebelling against his lord in various parts of the country. This terrible way of punishing a person convicted of treason was to be used for the next 500 years.

Throughout this time, Edward was in excellent health. Scotland became of increasing interest to him, as the throne had become vacant on the death of the only direct descendant of Alexander of Scotland, a child known as the Maid of Norway. Her mother, Margaret of Scotland, had married Eric, King of Norway. On passage to Scotland this little princess died in Orkney. There were no fewer than 13 applicants for the vacant throne and Edward called a meeting at Norham, in Northumberland, to decide the issue. The strongest claimants were John Balliol and Robert Bruce. Balliol was supported by Edward and was duly crowned at Scone. He had agreed to do homage for his kingdom to Edward.

At this time we still read of Edward being in excellent health. In 1294 there was another revolt by the Welsh, which was immediately crushed. Then the French seized Gascony. Edward was prevented from going to France, since Balliol had formed an alliance with France and rebelled. Once again Edward invaded Scotland and soon defeated Balliol, who was deposed and taken to the Tower of London. Here he lay for several years, eventually being exiled to France. Edward now declared himself King of Scotland and returned to London with the Stone of Scone on which the Scottish kings had been crowned. (This stone rested under the coronation chair in Westminster Abbey until 1996, when it was returned to Edinburgh.) Scotland was then to rise again under William Wallace. Again Edward attacked Scotland and at Falkirk defeated Wallace, who was captured and executed. In 1303 Robert Bruce and John Comyn were claimants to the Scottish throne. Bruce murdered Comyn at a meeting in a church and so began his claim. Edward defeated Bruce, who was forced into exile in Ireland.

It is at this point that we find all is not well with Edward. By 1306 he developed a complaint which contemporary writers describe as 'a dysentery', coming on late in that year. By this they implied a 'bloody flux', the passage of blood and mucus in his stools. These symptoms in a man of his age – he was now 67 – are frequently due to cancer of the rectum. Edward became progressively more ill. He lost weight and had no energy, to such an extent that soon he was unable to ride his horse and had to be carried in a litter. There was no associated vomiting and he was still able to eat, although he did lose weight. He does not appear to have had any fever, which would have been present if he had been suffering from an infected condition or from dysentery as we know it. It seems that it was plain both to Edward and to his physicians that the condition was incurable. However, he was not one to give up easily and he decided to continue with this intended attack on Scotland.

His illness became more marked as he approached the border, and he became progressively weaker, having been ill for some seven months. He rested for a short while at Carlisle, but wishing to push on, he continued in a litter. Froissart asserts that he ordered that if he were to die, his body was to be boiled down, so that his bones could be carried before his army into Scotland. He asked that his heart be taken by 100 knights to the Holy Land.

At the small town of Burgh by Sands his party halted as the King was in dire straits. Thomas Walsingham writes:

The King began to be troubled with dysentery and gave up hope of living longer. This disease increased on the morrow, that is to say Saturday. Bidding farewell to the present life he ended his days in well-doing, and his years in England.

On 6 July 1307 the King died, most probably from cancer of the rectum.

His tomb is in Westminster Abbey. Starkly made in black Purbeck marble, it is inscribed: 'Edward the First, Hammer of the Scots'. Eleanor's tomb is also in the abbey, the bronze-gilt effigy being one of the finest achievements of Gothic metalwork.

On 2 May 1774 Edward's tomb was opened and the body was found to be intact and in a 'reasonable state of preservation'. It was resealed without any detailed inspection of the body.

Edward II

 ~

Born Caernarfon, 1284
Murdered Berkeley Castle, February 1327

E DWARD II was the eldest son of Edward I and inherited many problems. The country was in a poor financial position and the war with Scotland had not been brought to a satisfactory conclusion. The position of the king was, however, very secure with strong allegiance from all the most powerful barons. Young Edward was in London when his father died at Burgh by Sands and he did not continue his father's efforts to subdue Scotland, turning his attention instead to domestic matters.

Edward was a very attractive prince, being some 6 feet tall with fair hair, a strong build and good general health. Before his accession he became very friendly with a certain Piers Gaveston. This young man had come over from France with his father, a Gascon knight who was in the service of Edward I. Shortly before Edward I died, he quarrelled with his son over this young man. Apparently, Edward wanted his father to give Ponthieu, a rich province, as a gift to his friend Gaveston. In order that he might be successful, he sent the request by Bishop Walter Langton, who was high in his father's favour. Edward I was enraged and shouted at his son, calling him a baseborn whoreson. Obviously Edward did not approve of the friendship, which was later to be one of the chief factors in the younger Edward's downfall.

As soon as Edward was on the throne he made Gaveston Earl of Cornwall, granting him all the income derived from that holding. The 23-year-old King's attitude to Gaveston naturally gives rise to the speculation about the King's sexuality. He could not bear to be separated from his friend and heaped honours upon him. Gaveston, meanwhile, did much to make himself unpopular. He was arrogant and gave insulting nicknames to the chief barons; for example, he called the Earl of Warwick the 'Black Dog of Ardenne'. To make matters worse, Gaveston was an expert in the lists and at a tournament he defeated Warenne, Pembroke, Hereford and Lancaster. In 1308, when Edward went to his marriage in France, he left Gaveston as regent. It was this marriage that caused Edward's final fall.

When Edward returned from France, accompanied by his new wife, Isabella, he rushed into the arms of his favourite. What she thought is not recorded, but Gaveston became more and more unpopular and the barons determined to destroy him. Twice they managed through Parliament to have Gaveston banished and twice he managed to return with the King's blessing. He was, however, finally banished with the sentence that he would forfeit his life by returning. He did so under the King's protection, and both he and Edward were confronted by the barons at York. Gaveston was placed in Scarborough Castle for his safety, but the castle was unable to withstand an attack by the Earl of Pembroke, whom Gaveston had ridiculed as 'Joseph the Jew'. On the understanding that he would be given quarter, Gaveston surrendered. He was immediately taken south and given into the custody of the Earl of Warwick. Imprisoned in Warwick Castle, he was tried and condemned. He was stabbed to death and his head cut off. On receiving this news, Edward was prostrate with grief and had the body brought to Windsor to be buried with all pomp.

Edward's young queen married him at the age of 12, so it is possible that initially there was no sexual relationship. She was said to be very beautiful, and her relationship with Edward must have been very difficult with Gaveston so obviously his favourite. Nonetheless, Edward was obviously able to enjoy married life with his queen, who was to have two sons and two daughters. In 1313 she had her first son, but the arrival of further 'favourites' was to bring about a final alienation.

A certain Hugh Despenser, an old and much respected nobleman, had a son also called Hugh, who became Edward's next favourite. Interestingly, Isabella's hatred seems to have extended to the father as well as the son. Again Edward heaped honours and lands on the Despensers and used them as his advisers so that they were greatly resented by all the barons. Edward seems to have been completely unable to realise that his behaviour was bound to lead to a confrontation. Finally the Earl of Lancaster led a large force to St Albans and demanded the exile of the Despensers. Father and son were duly banished.

The following year a force loyal to Edward defeated Lancaster at the Battle of Boroughbridge. Lancaster and Leicester, who had been involved in the death of Gaveston, were both executed and so Edward got his revenge. Roger Mortimer, one of the rebel knights, was imprisoned in the Tower of London, but he managed to escape. This was to prove of the greatest importance, leading finally to the death of the King.

The two Despensers were recalled. Their recall may well have been the final straw for the queen. Edward should have gone to France to pay homage for some of his French possessions to Philip, but fearing for his own safety he passed the lands into the name of his son. Still quarrelling with France, he hit on the unfortunate idea of sending his wife to see if she could have influence with her brother in bringing about a reconciliation. Accordingly, Isabella went to the French court of her brother and there she remained.

The young Prince of Wales was now 13 and he could do homage for the English lands in France. Accordingly, Edward sent his son across to France after his mother. At the French court Isabella met the young Roger Mortimer and they became lovers, leading to the unusual state of affairs of a queen of England being an acknowledged adulteress. Edward sent urgent orders that his wife and child should return to him, but Philip was unwilling to send his sister back unless she so wished.

Edward was now in a very difficult position. He did not have the strength to meet any armed challenge, as he had lost the support of most of the barons, his actions with the Despensers having made him most unpopular. It was obvious to Isabella that she would be backed if she now proclaimed that the Prince of Wales should usurp Edward, who had proved himself unfit to rule. Accordingly, Isabella landed on 26 September 1326 and was enthusiastically welcomed. Although she had landed with a very small force, she soon had a great following, including some of the King's brothers. Edward fled to Bristol Castle with the Despensers, but was soon

defeated and the elder Despenser was captured, later to be sum-
marily executed.

Edward and the younger Despenser tried to flee to Lundy Island,
but were driven by the weather to south Wales, where Edward was
betrayed and taken into custody at Kenilworth Castle. The younger
Despenser was taken to Hereford and there hanged, drawn and
quartered as a traitor. His 'private parts were cut off', which again is
possibly of some significance.

At the parliament held on 7 January 1327, the young Prince of
Wales was proclaimed and a long list of charges were brought
against Edward, most of which were somewhat ridiculous. A depu-
tation was sent to Kenilworth to secure the formal abdication of the
King; this he is said to have given under protest. The young King
was crowned on 29 January at Westminster, the first time in the history of England that a queen and her son displaced their husband
and father and held him prisoner. It was obvious that the fate of
Edward was sealed and that he would have to be disposed of at the
earliest opportunity.

The need for this became even more pressing when certain
monks began preaching against Isabella, saying that she should
join the King in his captivity and that she was an adulteress. Plots
were also started against Roger Mortimer who, with the queen, was
assuming the responsibility of government. Edward was in the custody of the Earl of Leicester, who treated him with respect. Morton
removed him from the charge of the earl and placed him under the
care of Sir John Maltravers and Sir Thomas Gournay, both of
whom had suffered in the cause of Lancaster. The King was moved
from one castle to another and was subject to various insults,
including having his beard shaved. He finally came to the Castle of
Berkeley, on the banks of the River Severn near Gloucester. Here he
was under the care of Gournay and Sir William Ogle.

On the night of 20 February, screams were heard coming from
the castle, as Edward was murdered. It is said that he was held down
by means of a heavy door placed on him and while so imprisoned, a
horn was pushed into his rectum and a hot iron passed through it,
so as to burn the walls of the bowel. (This method of killing a man
was also later used for the assassin of Henry IV of France.) In his
Chronicle John Capgrave writes:

In this same year was this old Edward slain with a hot spit put into his body, which could not be spied when he was dead for they put a horn into his tewhel and the spit through the horn that there should be no burning appear outside. This was by the ordinance as was said of Sir John Maltravers and Thomas Gournay, which laid a great door upon him while they did their work.

Edward had four children by Isabella: Edward, Prince of Wales, who succeeded him, and John, who was Earl of Cornwall, but who died as a young man. The elder daughter married King David Bruce of Scotland and the younger a prince of Guelders.

His son seems to have had some remorse, as he buried his father in a splendid tomb in Gloucester Cathedral which became a shrine of pilgrimage. The revenues from this shrine financed much of the fine stonework in the perpendicular style at Gloucester.

A strange tale is told by a papal notary who wrote to Edward III, telling him that the servants at Berkeley Castle came to Edward II while he was a prisoner and informed him of a plot to kill him. They advised that he dress in their old clothes and so escape. This he did and passed through the castle to the outer door, where he had to kill the porter for the keys. The knights who had come to kill him now feared the indignation of the queen for having failed to do so. They took the body of the murdered porter, extracted the heart as commanded, and, placing the rest of the body in a box, passed it off as that of the dead King. Thus the porter was buried in Gloucester Cathedral, and the King lived for a further two years in a hermitage. Although this seems a somewhat unlikely story, it is worth noting that the method of murder was such that no signs of injury could be found on the body. Moreover, the young King took no revenge on the murderers of his father, although he appears to have truly repented his death.

Nonetheless, it is accepted that Edward was murdered in Berkeley Castle by perforation of the bowel. He was dead the morning after the attack. This is itself unusual because death after such an injury normally follows in some days' time when perforation of the gut leads to peritonitis and associated damage to surrounding structures such as the bladder.

It seems that Edward's own death was very terrible, although not so terrible when considered by the brutal standards of the time. Neither side gave quarter to the other. Hate seems to have run very deep and emotions to have been very marked. The method used to kill him, through the rectum, may well have had a bearing on his homosexuality. We find in the following reign that his son and heir soon wished to rid himself of his mother and her lover, who were responsible for the death of his father.

The question as to whether Edward II was homosexual or not may be inferred by a consideration of some points in his history.

As a young man, it is said that he devoted himself to rowing and to driving chariots and he also spent much time as a craftsman making pits and roofing houses. All these seem to have been innocent enough, but he was told that they were not the pursuits for a future king. It was recorded that he did not resemble his august father and that he busied himself with vanities and frivolities.

His first favourite, Piers Gaveston, was a very attractive youth with great charm and great wit. Even his nicknames for important lords, while provoking hostility, amused Edward, who was not impressed by the dour court of his father. Edward's obvious delight in the company of Gaveston and his embracing and 'touching' were obvious to all, as was his wish to have him constantly in attendance. Edward's grief when he was separated from Gaveston by his banishment is also clear. Queen Isabella obviously resented him from their first meeting and her hatred for both him and the Despensers must have come from a deep resentment such as would be occasioned in a wife with a bisexual husband.

There is no doubt that Edward was capable of being a normal heterosexual husband. Although he had four children it is interesting that he took no mistresses throughout his life, which is very unusual for his time. And there is no record in his youth of him being concerned with 'ladies'.

He took great care in the burial of Gaveston at Windsor, where he had four bishops in attendance, but 'few of the princes of this world were willing to attend'. If the relationship of King and favourite were normal, why should they not attend? It would seem that they thought it immoral and at this time homosexuality was considered to be intensely immoral. This would also explain the deep resentment of the nobles who set out to kill Gaveston and who had no compunction about murdering him.

Edward III

~

Born Windsor, 13 November 1312
Died Sheen, 21 June 1377

After the Parliament the King, whom excessive impairment of old age had oppressed for a long time, rapidly became more troubled. For he fell into a weakness not of the kind that is believed to be usual in old men, but which is said to attach itself for the most part to youths given to lechery. But the cure of that disease is far more difficult in an old man than in a young one, for the different reasons of the old mans chilliness and the young mans heat. And, therefore the Lord King was weakened the more because the natural fluid and nutritive heat in him were now exhausted, and his virility failed. In truth it is said by many that he developed this disorder owing to his desire for that wanton baggage Alice Perrers, who had been kept from his presence. This was proved later on, for he took Alice back into their old relation. During this time the King's weakness increased and he began to be despaired of by his physicians, although the before mentioned courtesan along with her daughter Isabella had lain with him all night long. (*Chronicon Anglia*, writer unknown)

E DWARD III was to reign from 1327 to 1377. He came to the throne on the murder of his father when he was only 14. His mother and her lover, Roger Mortimer, held the reins of power and were to do so for three years. In his youth Edward was a very fine figure, being 6 feet tall, lithe and well built. He delighted in jousts and took part whenever possible. In 1330, with 12 knights, he took on all comers for three days.

Shortly afterwards, a parliament was called at Nottingham, and here Edward saw his chance to overthrow Mortimer. He managed to gain entry to the castle where Mortimer and Isabella were lodged by passing through a secret tunnel. There he captured Mortimer and took him to the Tower of London, from which he had escaped during the reign of Edward II. This time there was no escape and Mortimer was executed. Isabella was retired with a suitable pension to Castle Rising, and there she was to remain for 26 years, forgotten by all except her son, who visited her once a year and maintained her in something like regal state.

Edward's health was excellent and he continued to delight in all things appertaining to chivalry. He was greatly interested in the Arthurian legend and established a Round Table of 300 knights. He also established the Order of the Garter. In the sixteenth century Polydore Vergil tells the following story: at a ball held in Calais to celebrate its fall, a woman lost her garter. The King picked it up, with the words, 'Honi soit qui mal y pense'. Although this story was rejected by the historian of the order, Elias Ashmole, it is most attractive; the woman in question is identified as Joan, the Fair Maid of Kent, who was later to marry the Black Prince.

Edward's interest in jousting and tournaments led to their becoming a feature of his reign. He himself was a most active participant and may well have suffered some injuries; his mental deterioration in later life is possibly due to head injuries received in this way. He had a reckless addiction to the sport, although his dearest friend William Montague, Earl of Salisbury, was killed in a joust in 1344. The King never rejected a challenge, even from persons of inferior standing.

Edward married Philippa of Hainault and the marriage was very happy for over 30 years. The history of Philippa's intercession to save the burghers of Calais shows her to advantage. Shortly after the Battle of Crécy, Edward attacked and captured Calais, and then decided to take revenge on 12 of its burghers. Philippa, saying that she had never before asked for favours, now asked that they be given to her to do with as she thought fit. The request was granted and Philippa liberated the men.

By Philippa he had no fewer than 12 children. They were very healthy, with nine of them living to adult life, but none were to ascend the throne. The eldest child was the Black Prince, the father of Richard II; the sixth was John of Gaunt, Duke of Lancaster, the father of Bolingbroke, later Henry IV. During his reign, the Black Death was to decimate the country. However, the court was fortunate and Edward and his immediate family were not affected.

Edward undertook a massive building programme. Work at Ely, such as the Octagon, and at Windsor and Westminster went at a fast pace. He was fortunate in having William of Wykeham to help in this work. William first came into royal service as keeper 'of the kings eight digs at Windsor'. He was, however, of great ability and soon rose in importance, eventually being called upon to satisfy the King's taste for magnificence. An example is the splendid tomb he constructed for Edward II at Gloucester, which was to become a place of pilgrimage. He also developed the college quadrangle at Windsor, a concept which he used later when founding New College at Oxford.

Edward led an expedition against France in 1355, but returned to England, leaving his son the Black Prince to head the expedition in force in the later part of the year. At Poitiers, on 17 September, his army met that of the French King, John. The English, protected by archers, took up a defensive position and John made the great mistake of attacking this formation, on foot, in the open. The French were destroyed and John was captured and brought to England for ransom. Edward's reign continued as one of progress and success up to 1364, but from that date onwards, there is a noticeable change.

This change is associated with the health of the King. At this time he took a certain Alice Perrers as his mistress. She seems to have exerted a great influence over him and took an increasing control in his affairs. In the *Chronicon Anglia*, quoted at the head of this chapter, there is the implication that she might have had a disease which she transmitted to the King, one that is more common in 'young men'. Presumably a venereal infection is meant. Alice, however, had children by Edward and they do not appear to have had any such infection. Nevertheless, the King became much less active, neglecting his administrative work and seeming to slip into a prolonged dotage. This was accentuated by the death of his wife, Philippa, at Windsor, in 1369. With the removal of her strong sense of responsibility of kingship Edward's decline accelerated.

Meanwhile his son the Black Prince won a notable victory in

Spain in 1367. His marriage to Joan, the Fair Maid of Kent, who had twice been widowed previously, seems to have been a love match and there are many writings of their happiness together. However, by 1369 the prince developed an illness which left him unable to ride and led to progressive weakness and debility. He returned to England in 1371 and from this date seems to have taken a decreasing part in all affairs. It must have been a great sadness for his father to see his illustrious son become so debilitated. The prince was to die in 1376; his very beautiful tomb and armour are in Canterbury Cathedral. His son Richard was to become King.

Edward's family was now diminished, and most responsibility was passed to his son John of Gaunt. From a military point of view, England was forced on the defensive and affairs in France went badly. Parliament, which had been easy to control while the country was victorious, became a hive of intrigue. As Edward's reign drew to a close, John of Gaunt had great difficulty in maintaining stability.

In his dotage, the King was taking very little part in affairs. It is probable that he had cerebral vascular disease, associated with a mild stroke. This is implied by the quotation, and it is true that venereal disease does give rise to cerebral vascular degeneration. There is, however, a difficulty in ascribing his troubles to syphilis, as none of his children appear to have suffered from it, and although Alice Perrers is much maligned, there is no real evidence that she had any such trouble. There is no doubt, however, that the King had a lingering death for he developed a beard and long flowing hair while lying at Sheen, where he continued throughout the spring and early summer of 1377, finally dying on 21 June.

A wooden effigy of the King, painted and dressed as in life, was placed on his bier. This still survives and is of great interest, as the face was probably carved from a death mask. The carving shows that the mouth is twisted from a facial paralysis, no doubt following a stroke. We do not know when this took place, but a previous stroke (cerebral haemorrhage or thrombosis) would account for his altered character and his dotage. History does not record such a stroke, although we can be fairly certain that Edward did indeed have one and that it contributed to his mental changes and death. His death can therefore be ascribed to cerebral vascular disease, resulting in a cerebral thrombosis which damaged the right side of the brain. Most people who have this condition develop terminal bronchopneumonia. At his death, he was very much alone, with only his confessor to comfort him.

John of Gaunt, the faithful son, was to see that Edward was buried along with his wife at Westminster Abbey. There his beautiful bronze effigy shows an old man with long flowing hair and beard, radiating serenity.

Richard II

~

Born Bordeaux 13 April 1367
Died Pontefract, 14 February 1400

O UR MEMORY of the death of Richard II is confused by
Shakespeare. In his excellent play of Richard's life and death,
he has Richard struck down fighting for his life. In fact, there is no
evidence to support this type of death and more recent examination of his skeleton excludes severe damage to his skull. His death
was definitely associated with food, either by what he was given to
eat or, which is less likely, by starvation.

> The common frame is that he was every day served at table with
> costly meat like a King, and again when the meat was set before
> him he was forbidden once to touch it and so died of force of
> famine. But Walsingham referreth it altogether to voluntary pin-
> ing of himself. One writer saith that he was felled with a stroke of a
> poleaxe which Sir Piers gave upon the head and therewith rid him
> of life. (*Holinshed Chronicle*)

Richard Plantagenet was born at Bordeaux, a healthy and greatly
cherished child, the son of the Black Prince and Joan, the Fair Maid
of Kent. A curious legend was to arise that he was born without a
skin and had to be nourished in the skin of goats. What this signi-
fies is not clear, as he was a healthy young boy who was to succeed
his grandfather, Edward III, when he was ten years of age.

The country was in a very unstable condition following
Edward's long dotage. The young Richard was faced with the
Peasants' Revolt when he was merely 14 and the reports of this show

both his personal courage and his devious character: the promises he made to the mob to get it to withdraw were never kept. The country was governed by John of Gaunt, who was far from popular and who was, to some extent, responsible for Richard's eventual 'failure'. Further difficulties were caused by the prolonged war with France and by the terrible Black Death, which caused a sudden and severe reduction in the available rural workforce, thus upsetting the stable rural economy.

In his youth, Richard became very fond of wearing jewellery and elaborate and costly dress. He was responsible for the extravagant fashion in footwear with a very elongated toe piece and he also used what was known as a 'kerchief'; in fact, he could be said to be the inventor of the handkerchief. His elaborate and colourful dress made him very different from his warlike father and indeed it has been suggested that he was not the son of the Black Prince, but the result of an affair which the Fair Maid had while in France with a 'gentleman of the court'. However, this seems unlikely because the Black Prince and his wife seem to have been very much in love and took obvious delight in their son.

Richard grew up into a tall and handsome man, with fair hair. In 1382 he married Anne of Bohemia, apparently securing her as a wife by paying a very substantial sum to her father, so substantial that it was said he had bought her rather than received her as a 'gift'. He developed a very deep affection for Anne and displayed a violent grief at her early death in 1394, very characteristic of the excessive emotional reactions of the Plantagenet dynasty.

Richard was a scholar with a great love for books and literature. Rather than holding jousts, his court was entertained with songs and dances, and clothing became more and more elaborate. Geoffrey Chaucer, who had previously worked for Edward III, was attached to his court and became Clerk of the King's Works in 1389, taking an active part in Richard's great building programme. Chaucer, like so many of Richard's party, was to change sides when Richard was deposed; it was even suspected that the man responsible for Richard's death was the nephew of Chaucer's wife. Richard quarrelled with many powerful persons: his chancellor, Thomas Arundel; Richard Scrope, Archbishop of York; William Courtney, Archbishop of Canterbury; and even John of Gaunt. After his quarrel with John of Gaunt he ordered the duke's execution, but

Gaunt rode to Sheen with armed support and they had a tense reconciliation.

Richard had two favourites, Robert de Vere and, later, Michael de la Pole, and he was suspected of having 'Edward II vice'. Both the favourites had to escape to exile and while in Louvain, Robert de Vere died. Richard had his body embalmed and brought home in a scented coffin, which was then opened so that Richard could clasp his fingers. This caused the King further unpopularity.

Several persons led by Thomas Woodstock, Earl of Gloucester, formed a group called the Appellants, who became very powerful with the support of Parliament. Richard, who then had the support of John of Gaunt, decided to assume responsibility and work for peace with Ireland. He went there to meet the local kings and secured a measure of agreement for his plans, but then his queen died at the early age of 27. Richard was so affected that he ordered the palace at Sheen, the place of her death, completely destroyed.

To secure peace with France, Richard was now betrothed to the daughter of the King, a child of six called Isabelle. Her marriage to Richard took place when she was seven. Richard had no heir, and it was obvious that she would not be able to produce a child for some considerable time. The recognised heir became Roger Mortimer, Earl of March; he was the son of Philippa, the granddaughter of Edward III, by his second son Lionel, Duke of Clarence. March died in 1398, leaving the throne in dispute. His daughter, Anne Mowbray, later married Richard, Earl of Cambridge, son of the Duke of York, thus uniting the lines of two of Edward's sons. This line was to become the Yorkist line in the Wars of the Roses.

Richard was in good health and, being reasonably young, had no doubt that he would live long enough to have issue from Isabelle. He seems to have been unaware of the gathering threats to his throne and he continued to attack the Appellants for their affronts. That said, two of their number, Mowbray and Bolingbroke, now the Dukes of Hereford and Norfolk, appeared to be safe from attack since their power was such as might be needed by the King. They seem to have been unaware that Richard was biding his time until he could take his revenge. His opportunity came when Bolingbroke reported a conversation he had with Mowbray while riding together in London. There was apparently a plot to remove both Bolingbroke and his father, John of Gaunt. The father advised a counterattack, but Bolingbroke, not wanting to get involved, brought the matter to Richard. He was made to repeat the charge to Parliament and a committee was appointed to consider it.

The committee met in Bristol, but were unable fully to support the charges, as they said there was insufficient evidence. It was decided that the matter should be referred to the Court of Chivalry – in other words, to trial by combat. The possibility of a duel to the death between a cousin of the King and the Earl Marshal of England was an encounter of the greatest import. To Richard there must have appeared an obvious danger: if Bolingbroke were to win, his popularity was so great that he might easily threaten Richard; if he lost, his father, John of Gaunt, would be mortally offended. On the other hand, the occasion did present to Richard the possibility that one of the greatest Appellants might well be eliminated. According to Froissart, Richard's advisers warned that he should not get involved, but in the mind of the King this was an opportunity to eliminate them both, possibly at no danger to himself.

Bolingbroke, a large and powerful man, had armourers from Lombardy to supply his weapons, while Mowbray obtained his from Germany. Shakespeare certainly recognised a good scene for his play and used the great event, which had all and sundry present. Bolingbroke entered first on a white horse, followed by Mowbray. The joust was on the point of taking place when the King halted matters by throwing down his staff.

After two hours' discussion, the King decreed that Bolingbroke be exiled for ten years and Mowbray for life. It looked as if the King had rid himself of two enemies at little cost. Mowbray set off on a pilgrimage to Jerusalem, but died in Venice a year after his banishment. Bolingbroke took up residence at the French court in September 1398.

By February of 1399, John of Gaunt had died and circumstances were dramatically altered. Bolingbroke should now have inherited the vast Lancastrian estates of his father, but Richard recalled a parliamentary committee which extended the exile to life. It also confiscated the estates, which were to revert to the Crown. Thus Richard set Bolingbroke on the path which was to lead to his own death.

A campaign in Ireland drew Richard away from England and gave Bolingbroke a chance to land. This he immediately did, gain-ing widespread support. The Lancastrian cause of the Gaunt family was very powerful and even the Duke of York, who had been left to rule in Richard's place, declared for Bolingbroke. Richard underestimated the danger on his return. Passing north along the Welsh border to Chester, where he had always found support, he reached the almost impregnable Conway Castle. There he met with the Earl of Northumberland, who as Bolingbroke's spokesman guaranteed him free passage to Flint Castle, where he was to meet with Bolingbroke. Richard agreed to leave Conway, but while on his way to the castle he was ambushed. He was first taken to Flint and from there to the Tower of London, where he was imprisoned and forced to abdicate. Shakespeare gives him the following thoughts: 'My God, a wonderful land is this, and a fickle, which has exiled, slain, destroyed and ruined so many Kings, rulers and great men, and is ever tainted with strife and variance and envy.'

At this time, Richard was 32 and evidently in very good health, being able to ride the long distances to Wales and London. This must have worried Bolingbroke, who was further disturbed when a committee was established to consider his claim to the throne. They agreed that he had a right by default and by conquest, but not by rightful inheritance. Bolingbroke tried to show that the Black Prince was not the eldest son of Edward III, who had had an elder child ignored because of deformity. This was not substantiated, making Bolingbroke's position less strong, particularly while Richard lived. The correct succession should have passed the crown to the descendants of Lionel, Duke of Clarence, the second son of Edward III. This claim had passed to his daughter, Philippa, who was married to Roger Mortimer. As mentioned, their son, also called Roger, was considered throughout Richard's reign to be the rightful heir if Richard should have no sons. This made Bolingbroke's position even more insecure, so it became increasingly obvious that to consolidate his position, he had to eliminate Richard.

Richard was forcibly disguised as a simple forester and taken from the Tower of London to Leeds Castle in Kent. It was in the north that Bolingbroke was strongest, so it was decided to move him to Pontefract. It was obvious that he had to die, but how? Shakespeare has Exton and servants attacking the King, who slays two of the servants before being struck down by Exton with a poleaxe. It was obvious that Shakespeare had to make the death, which was being brought about by the father of his great hero, Henry V, appear reasonable and not due to any underhand method such as poison. In his chronicle, Holinshed also suggests the possibility that Richard was killed with a poleaxe, but this method would not have suited Henry Bolingbroke, who was later to expose the body of Richard when it was carried through England to show that the King had died a natural death.

Indeed, there is no evidence of any sign of violence on the body and several drawings of the funeral show the exposed head of Richard without any evidence of injury. In fact, examination of the skull at a later date completely rules out the possibility of death due to a head injury.

The official line was that Richard had refused to eat, although others said that he had been prevented from eating, suggesting starvation as a possible cause of death. However, there is no evidence of gross wasting of the body and, as a cause of death, starvation would take much longer than the ten days Richard took to die. Could it be that he was poisoned? This was a convenient way to destroy a prisoner and one in very common use since the days of Edward the Confessor. Certainly, it is interesting to note even Shakespeare hinting that such a strategy was considered, but he was unlikely to make a direct accusation against the father of Henry V. All kings had tasters to see that their food was not poisoned:

Scene V: Enter Keeper with a dish.

KEEPER My Lord will't please you to fall to
KING RICHARD Taste it first, as thou are wont to do
KEEPER My Lord, I dare not; Sir Pierce of Exton, who lately come from the King, commands the contrary
KING RICHARD The Devil take Henry of Lancaster and thee. Patience is stale and I weary of it

He strikes the keeper. Help, help, help. Enter Exton and Servants armed etc, etc.

It is thus impossible to be absolutely sure of the cause of Richard's death, although poisoning seems far the most likely. It appears that the King took some ten days to die, which points to a poison that leaves no outward sign. The most obvious would be the toadstool known as the death cap (*Amanita philodes*), a common enough poison which can be chopped up and incorporated in any food. It takes about ten days to result in death, and for this reason the death is often not attributed to the toadstool but is thought to be from a natural cause. The poison causes damage to both the kidneys and the liver and is thus not excreted, but circulates doing more and more damage. It is most difficult to eradicate and is extremely dangerous, even today, and the mortality rate is still very high in spite of all treatment. It is quite possible to mistake the toadstool for a common mushroom.

The funeral arrangements for Richard showed that Henry wished to do as much honour to him as was consistent with events. He was elaborately embalmed and wrapped in linen, then placed in a lead coffin with his face left bare, to be seen by all. On his passage from Pontefract to London, he was placed on a horse-drawn carriage, and covered with a black cloth with a banner at each corner: two of St George and two of his patron saint, Edward the Confessor. Torchbearers surrounded the carriage as it made its way to London, where Richard was escorted to St Paul's Cathedral to lie in state for two days. He was then buried by the Abbot of St Albans in the Dominican Priory of Kings Langley, which was probably chosen because Richard was very fond of the town, spending time there with his first wife; it was also the burial place of his brother Edward.

On the accession of Henry V, Richard was to be moved to his final resting-place in Westminster Abbey. Henry V was said to be very fond of Richard, having spent much of his youth in his court, and is said to have grown fonder of him than of his own father. Richard was to join his queen, Anne of Bohemia, in a great bronze tomb in Westminster. The tomb was not well constructed; in the course of time, several side plates became loose and it was possible to push items through holes into the tomb and even to see the enclosed bones. Some of these, including the jawbone, were removed. In 1880, the tomb was repaired and the various oddments therein removed. The missing jawbone was returned and the tomb was firmly sealed and closed.

With the death of Richard II the Plantagenet line ended. Henry IV was to start the Lancastrian line of kings.

Henry IV

~

Born 1366
Died Westminster, 20 March 1413

Henry IV became king by displacing and possibly murdering
Richard II. This is supported by the General and Exchequer
Council minutes of 1400 and by items from the issue roll of the
exchequer.

The Council minutes of 1400 recommend: 'If Richard formerly
king should still be living as was supposed, it should be ordered
that he should be securely guarded for the safety of the king's estate
and of his kingdom.' A further minute states: 'The king should be
advised, if Richard be living, that he should be placed in such a safe
keeping as the lords decreed and that, if he be dead, he should be
shown openly to the people so that they could have knowledge of
the fact.' It has come to light that the latter minute is a replacement
of a previous minute, one that was possibly even more damaging to
Henry. The following exchequer payments are even more incrimi-
nating:

> To William Loveney, clerk of the Great Wardrobe, sent to
> Pontefract Castle on secret business, by order of the King, 66s 8d.

> To a valet of Sir Thomas Swynford, coming from Pontefract to
> London, to certify to the king's council of certain matters which
> concern the kings advantage including the hire of a horse for
> speed 26s 8d.

These items seem to confirm that Henry was concerned with the
death of Richard and was personally involved. This knowledge was

to haunt Henry throughout his life and his prolonged illness in later life was attributed by him to his sins as a murderer.

As a young man, Henry was very well built and powerful, taller than average at 5 feet 10 inches. He was an excellent jouster and might well have won the celebrated joust with Mowbray if it had taken place. He does not appear to have suffered from any disease as a young man and at the time of his coronation was in excellent health. In spite of this, the shadow which lay over the whole of his reign appeared at his coronation, where it is reported: '…The same rotting did the anointing at his coronation portend; for there ensued such a growth of lice, especially on his head, that he neither grew hair, nor could he have his head covered for many months.'

He was anointed with holy oil kept in a golden eagle, which had been used for the first time for Richard II. At the coronation Henry also had a King's Champion, a member of the Dymoke family, who were to be the hereditary holders of the office. All efforts were made in order that the succession might appear to be correct. Still, Henry did not feel secure and the rebellions in support of Richard caused him reluctantly to sanction the murder.

This troubled him sorely, for the two cousins had been brought up together. Henry had stood by Richard, particularly during the Duke of Gloucester's revolt. As a reward for his support, Henry had been made Duke of Hereford, and it was as Hereford that he quarrelled with Norfolk, leading to the fateful joust at Coventry.

Henry was driven by events along the fateful road which was to make him King. His guilt was brought about as much by Richard's scheming as by his own doings. Henry would have been content to see Richard live in retirement, if it hadn't been for the rebellions to restore Richard which kept breaking out.

One event in particular preyed on Henry's mind. While Richard was in Conway Castle, he had been visited by Henry's representatives. Their mission was to persuade the King to leave Conway, an almost impregnable fortress, so that he could then be ambushed. Suspicious, Richard asked these representatives to swear that no harm was intended to him and that he would be given free passage to Chester. On Henry's behalf the representatives swore safe conduct, unaware that they were swearing on sacred bones which had been placed under their hands. For the oath to be broken would be sacrilege. It was, of course, and Richard was ambushed and taken prisoner. Henry was informed of the sacrilege and this added to his marked depression.

As King, Henry married Lady Mary de Bohun, by whom he had six children. The eldest surviving son was to become Henry V; the others were to become the Dukes of Clarence, Bedford and Gloucester. All were reasonably healthy, as were his two daughters. There is no doubt that, apart from some mental depression, Henry was of good health.

Then in 1404 his condition changed. A rebellion in the north saw his friends, including the Archbishop of York, revolt against him. Henry managed to defeat them, but he was particularly annoyed that these friends of his had rebelled against him. Against the advice of many, he executed the leaders, including the Archbishop of York. Never before had such a crime been committed against the Church and the Pope cursed all who had brought it about. Henry thus had another 'sin' to prey on his mind.

His relationship with his eldest son was also far from happy. At the same time as he had usurped the throne, his son Henry was returning from Ireland in the retinue of Richard II, where he had been placed for his education. The young Henry had become very fond of his uncle Richard and the struggle between the two men must have upset him. It was even said that the son had become fonder of his uncle than of his own father. This meant an additional psychological burden for the King.

It was at this time that Henry became ill. His fine appearance became marred by a progressive skin disease. At first he thought it was a 'leprosy', but it was not. The condition was offensive as well as unattractive, although fortunately it did not affect his face or his hands and his clothes covered the disease; however, to Henry it appeared to be a divine visitation for the offences he had committed. It was also possibly the cause of his estrangement from his wife.

To appease the Church and possibly get some remission from his disease, Henry started to persecute the Lollards, a group of religious fanatics who were criticising the Church. He was most active in this and even Sir John Oldcastle, an old friend of the Prince of Wales, was executed. And yet, Henry was undoubtedly a sensitive person: there is an account of his trying to persuade one of the

Lollards, who was about to be burned, to recant and so avoid the flames. When the burning commenced, Henry was overcome with the cries of the martyr and ordered the flames to be put out. Again he tried to persuade the victim to recant; again the victim, although severely burnt, refused, so the poor chap was finally burnt to death.

Henry's skin condition was to progress for nine years, with periodic remissions and exacerbations. It did not appear to damage his health greatly in itself, and he was able to continue with his military preparations and live a normal life. His physicians were not able to do anything to help; he was given a variety of treatments, none of which had any effect. The condition would probably be described today as exfoliative dermatitis, although the possibility of it being lupus erythematosus cannot be excluded. In this condition, the immune responses of the patient are decreased and he is apt to fall victim to intercurrent infection. He was given a variety of treatments, none of which had any effect.

Some time around 1400, Henry started to have attacks resembling epileptic fits. These were followed by periods of unconsciousness, so that it was sometimes difficult to establish whether the King still lived or not. Unfortunately, we do not have any clear description of the attacks, but they are unlikely to have been true epileptic fits.

Henry was also troubled lest his two eldest sons should fight for the throne and repeat his own struggle with Richard. In Eltham Palace, in 1412, he is said to have called the Prince of Wales to him and made a melancholy speech to him saying he hoped that his two sons would not fight for the throne. He also made his will, which was of the utmost simplicity: he described himself as a 'sinful wretch' and made no elaborate arrangements for his own funeral or for his tomb, merely asking to be buried not in the abbey at Westminster but at Canterbury.

Henry's final illness took place as he went to pray at the tomb of the Confessor in the abbey at Westminster. He had one of his strange epileptiform attacks and was taken to lie in the abbot's lodging. As he recovered, he asked where he was and was told that he was in the Jerusalem Chamber. The King said: 'Praise be to the Father of Heaven, for now I know that I shall die in this chamber, according to the prophecy of me aforesaid that I should die in

Jerusalem.' At the time of the attack he was in the course of preparing for a journey to the Holy Land.

As he lay on a straw pallet near the fire in the Jerusalem Chamber, we are told that his confessor, John Tiklle, was called. It was suggested that the King repent for three things: the death of Richard; the execution of Richard Scrope, the Archbishop of York; and the usurpation of the crown. Henry replied: 'For the first poyntis I wrote onto the Pope and veri treuth of y conscions. Ane he sent me a bulle with absoltion and penauns assigned, whech I have fulfilled. As for the third poynt, it is hard to sette remedy, for my children will not suffer that the regalic go oute of oure lyneage.'

It would appear from this that Henry was in a reasonably conscious state. If his epilepsy had been due to the development of a cerebral tumour, a condition which does, in later life, give rise to such symptoms, then his death would have been characterised by increasing coma. He would also have had vomiting and severe headache, with a serious loss of vision. None of these seems to have been present, so we can exclude a brain tumour. However, epileptiform attacks may come about from uraemia, or kidney failure, which would also have complicated his severe skin problems, so this may well have been the cause of his prolonged terminal illness.

Monstrelet writes that as the end approached, it was the custom to place the crown near a dying king so that his successor could pick it up the moment the king died. When Henry appeared to have passed away, his attendants placed a cloth over his face and the Prince of Wales took the crown and left the room. Shortly afterwards, the King recovered and asked what had happened to the crown. His son returned and explained that he thought that his father was dead.

The King said: 'Good son, what right could you have to the crown, when I have none. And this you well know.'

'My lord', replied the prince, 'as you have held and kept it with the sword, so will I keep it as long as I live.'

And so Henry died. The cause of death would appear to be a uraemic termination of severe chronic exfoliative dermatitis, a severe skin condition.

The beautiful monument Henry has at Canterbury was placed

there by his second wife, Joan of Navarre. She commissioned Richard's architect, Henry Yevele, to make the alabaster effigy and the beautiful canopy.

At the time of his death, many thought that he was dying a leper. Congrave in his *Chronicle* writes: 'The king, after that time [1404] lost the beauty of his face. For, as the common opinion went, from that time until his death, he was a leper and even fouler and fouler. For in his death as they that saw him recorded he was so contracted that his body was scarce a cubit length.'

This, however, is contradicted by *Archaeologia* (of 1832, Vol. XXVI, p.444) where there is a description of the coffin being opened at Canterbury in 1832:

> The face of the deceased was seen in complete preservation. The nose elevated, the cartage even remaining, though on the admission of air it shrank away and had entirely disappeared before the examination was finished. The skin of the chin was entire, of the consistence and thickness of the upper leather of a shoe, brown and moist; the beard thick and matted, and of a deep russet colour. The jaws were perfect and all the teeth in them except one foretooth, which had probably been lost during the king's life. The surveyor stated that when he introduced his finger under the wrappings to remove them, he distinctly felt the orbits of the eyes prominent in their sockets. The flesh upon the nose was moist, clammy, and of the same brown colour as every other part of the face.

So we see that there was no possibility of Henry having leprosy. He was relatively young, being 46 at the time of his death. There is one further additional factor which should be considered. All persons who indulged in jousting, as Henry did, would have received many blows to the head. They would become, as do boxers, affected by this repeated injury in later life. The brain receives repeated small injuries or is damaged by bleeding in the skull, which causes a varying degree of brain damage resulting in altered behaviour and possible mild dementia. If there were local damage to brain tissue, epileptiform attacks could occur. The strange attacks which Henry suffered up to the time of his death might have resulted from this cause.

Henry V

~

Born Monmouth, 1387
Died Bois de Vincennes, 31 August 1422

H ENRY OF MONMOUTH was born in the gatehouse of Monmouth Castle, the eldest son of Henry IV. He was to die at the early age of 35 in France. His remains are buried at Westminster.

Just as Edward III was 'neglected' by Shakespeare, so Henry V was immortalised. The victories of Edward III and the Black Prince were just as, or more significant, and more lasting. But it is Henry V who is always remembered, as the great hero of the Battle of Agincourt, a battle he fought and won as part of his great personal ambition. Throughout his life, Henry was determined to unite the two thrones of England and France, even marrying to further his ambition. However, he actually achieved very little to advance his own country.

As a young man, Henry is said to have been very wild and to have upset his father, Henry IV, with his behaviour. *The English Chronicle* states: 'In his youth, he had been wild, reckless and sparing nothing of his lusts or desires, but accomplished them after his liking; but as soon as he was crowned, anointed and sacred, anon suddenly he changed into a new man.' It was perhaps as well for Henry that he did so, since by all accounts he was very lucky as a young man not to have contracted venereal disease. While a child at Monmouth Castle, he contracted a serious disease, the exact nature of which is unknown. It appears not to have had any lasting effect. In his will, Henry was to remember his old nurse, Joan Waring; was it she who nursed him in his serious childhood illness? Later, he was wounded in the face by an arrow at the Battle of Shrewsbury, but this again healed leaving no obvious scar, as seen in his later portraits. His father had been very anxious that he should not quarrel with his brother, the Duke of Clarence, over the throne. Clarence was a powerful and impressive personality, but the brothers, unlike so many others, were very sincere friends. Henry's portraits depict a very unimpressive individual, so much so that our present Queen is said to have remarked, 'Can that really be him?' Perhaps we have been taught to think of him in an exaggerated way by seeing films and plays of his exploits.

When Henry was crowned, he made it his life's work to confirm his claim to the French crown, too. Under Edward III and the Black Prince, the Battles of Crécy and Poitiers had been won, and with Charles of France suffering repeated attacks of insanity, the stage was set for Henry to seize the crown of France. His first campaign was to conclude at Agincourt.

The attack on France was directed through Harfleur, a town which was very heavily fortified and had to be taken by siege. It lay in a marsh in a very unhealthy district. The English were packed into a small area with no sanitation and within two weeks severe dysentery had broken out, affecting those of both high and low rank. The Earl of Suffolk died, as did the King's friend Richard Courtenay, the Bishop of Norwich. Clarence was so severely ill that he had to be sent home to England and only just managed to recover. Morale fell still further when August brought a heatwave which made life unbearable. Although Henry had brought a whole host of assistants, medical supplies and surgical instruments, some 2,000 men either died or were severely ill. Henry himself managed to stay free from any trouble, perhaps because he had three personal physicians. No women were allowed in the army train at Agincourt: a strict code of morals was followed as this whole expedition was designed to put Henry on the throne of France, after which he would lead a crusade to the Holy Land.

Harfleur was eventually captured, but Henry lost a great number of his troops, and of those that were left, many were severely debilitated. Disease had taken all but some 9,000 men-at-arms and some 5,000 archers, about half the force that had left England. The desperate march through France and the eventual Battle of

Agincourt are well known. This battle was fought and won against seemingly impossible odds, which fuelled Henry's obsession to obtain the crown of France.

The return crossing to England took place in terrible weather, but Henry was not upset or seasick. He did, however, have medicines sent out from England for the 'kings person', but what they were or why they were required we do not know. He seems to have been in excellent health. His homecoming to London was a great triumph although it was reported that Henry was 'most reserved and sober'.

In two years, Henry was back in France in pursuit of his goal. Victory at Agincourt had been of no strategic advantage, although it did prevent the French from destroying Henry. He then retook most of Normandy when the Duke of Burgundy was assassinated by supporters of the Dauphin. This gave Henry greatly increased support from the Burgundians.

To consolidate his position, Henry tried to arrange a marriage with the French princess, Catherine de Valois. Henry first met Catherine on 1 June 1419 and was so pleased with her that he sent her a gift of jewellery, which unfortunately was stolen in transit by bandits. His terms for the alliance were for him to inherit the French lands of Edward III, to retain all his conquests and to receive a dowry of 800,000 crowns. Negotiations failed and the war was continued.

In 1420 the French capitulated and the Treaty of Troyes was drawn up and signed by the two Kings. The treaty named Henry as King of France on the death of Charles VI and approved the marriage to Catherine with a dowry. Henry appeared to be nearing his life's ambition. He married Catherine and returned to England, safe now to consider a crusade to the Holy Land.

On 6 December 1421, Catherine gave birth to a son. This heir was born at Windsor, although Henry had been very anxious that he should be born at Westminster, as he attached great importance to the place of birth. The succession was now assured.

Unfortunately, it was at this stage that his brother Clarence, who had been sent home to recuperate, wanted to prove his prowess. He took a force over to France, only to be soon defeated, a serious matter (and perhaps inevitable since he had fought without archers). This forced Henry to return himself and in 1421 he laid siege to

Meaux. Here, as at Harfleur, dysentery broke out throughout the army and Henry also became very unwell.

From accounts, it appears he had a bloody flux. Thomas Walsingham writes: 'The king from having an old distemper, which he had contracted from excessive and long-continued exertion, meanwhile fell into an acute fever with violent dysentery. This his physicians did not venture to treat by any internal medication, but forthwith gave up hope of his life. On August 30th, his maker took back his soul.'

Others write that he had a disease of the fundament called St Anthony's Fire, while some refer to St Fiacre's disease. What this disease should be is not known. John de Fordun writes in *The Scottish Cronicon*: 'He was attacked by a cancerous disease which the peasantry called St Fiacres Ill'.

If Henry did indeed suffer from dysentery, it would most probably have been of a bacillary type and an acute exacerbation with toxic prostration and dehydration could have caused death. This is one of the accepted causes of Henry's death. However, there are several points in regard to the illness which do not fit in with such a diagnosis. Firstly, the illness was very prolonged. He was unwell for some time, losing considerable weight and becoming wasted. This is not typical of acute dysentery and suggests that his illness was a long-standing condition, rather than an acute infection. He lived long enough for Catherine to cross over from England to see him, although he never saw his son; his physicians knew that he was going to die and had sent for her. Secondly, his condition was of such a nature that his physicians did not venture to treat it and gave up all hope of his life. This would not be typical of dysentery, a disease which they saw so commonly and for which they gave continued treatment and were often able to cure. Henry's illness was of an 'incurable nature'. John de Fordun tells of his having a 'cancer' and this may well be the true cause of death. Cancer of the rectum would fit in with Henry's medical history and would produce some symptoms similar to dysentery. As dysenteric infection was so common at the time, it would be very easy for a cancer to be confused with the more common infection. The physicians seem to have realised that Henry did not have a common disease, but a disease from which he would die no matter what they did. It would be reasonable to say that death from dysentery may well have been correct, but the possibility of his also having cancer of the rectum should be considered as a distinct probability.

Had Henry survived for only one more month, all his ambitions would have been fulfilled. The French King, Charles VI, survived him for only that short time, so Henry would have become King of France and England.

On his death his body was not embalmed but dismembered. The various parts of the corpse were boiled down to the bones, with the liquid part sent to a local abbey and the bones carefully taken in procession back to England. A complete death mask of head and body was made in boiled leather and fitted on top of his bier. The mask was crowned and carried an orb and sceptre. These arrangements were so elaborate that they must have been made some time before his death. This again shows there was ample warning of the outcome of his illness, which supports the possibility of his terminal cancer of the rectum.

Back in England, Catherine commissioned a silver effigy for his tomb. It was made in wood and covered in silver, with a solid silver head. He was buried in the Henry V Chantry Chapel at Westminster Abbey, where his sword, shield and broken battle helm are displayed. The silver and the solid silver head were removed during the reign of Henry VIII, when Henry was despoiling the abbeys.

Henry's widow Catherine was eventually to marry Owen ap Meredyth ap Tudor and found the Tudor dynasty. Considering her importance, her final history is somewhat bizarre. She was the daughter of a king, the wife of a king, the mother of a king and the grandmother of a king. She was of small stature and apparently of a pleasant and easy disposition. She was a devoted mother, but probably transmitted to her son, the infant King Henry VI, depressive psychosis, a form of madness. Catherine lived until 1437, when she died in Bermondsey Abbey after an illness of some six months' duration.

There was naturally some difficulty in her burial place, because she was no longer the wife of Henry V, and so could not be interred in the Chantry Chapel. Her 'failing' was that on the death of her royal husband she fell in love with a commoner, Tudor. She married him in secret, as it was very likely that if the truth were known, his life would have been in peril. It was her sons by Tudor – Edmund, later Earl of Richmond, and Jasper, Earl of Pembroke – who were to be father and uncle of Henry VII. Thus her son by her first husband was Henry VI and her grandson by her second husband Henry VII.

As Catherine had founded the Tudor line, one would have expected the Tudors to show the greatest respect for her body, if only to assure their own claim to kingship. However, Catherine was buried in a plain tomb in front of the altar at Westminster.

It appears that this was regarded as a temporary place, since the *Chronicles of Westminster* show that her son, Henry VI, later visited the abbey with a view to deciding where he should be buried. The original site of Catherine's tomb, close to the high altar, was of the greatest importance, while the tomb itself was bare and unsightly. It was suggested that it might be moved a little lower down to make room for the King. It could then be suitably decorated and inscribed. However, Henry eventually chose for himself a site in the abbey close to the tomb of Henry III, but after his death his wishes apparently held no importance and were not respected.

Later still, Henry VII twice visited the abbey with a view to arranging for his own place of burial. He chose to be buried in front of the high altar, so Catherine was disinterred and her coffin placed behind the high altar, probably with a view to her being placed in some other part of the abbey at a later date. He intended to make her plain tomb more resplendent, as he was always most anxious to impress his claim to the throne and used Catherine to strengthen that claim. By an oversight, however, Catherine was left unburied. After the death of Henry VII the responsibility rested with Henry VIII who had no sympathy for the abbey or its contents, deciding to be buried himself at Windsor. He would not spare the money for a costly tomb for Catherine; he even removed the silver from the tomb of Henry V, including the silver head.

Poor Catherine was to remain without a grave until 1793. The box coffin in which she lay was left in place behind the altar and it was possible for persons to request a 'view' from the verger, who would then show them the body. On his 36th birthday, 23 February 1669, Samuel Pepys decided to visit the theatre with his family. He ordered a conveyance, but decided, as it was Shrove Tuesday, to visit the abbey and view the royal tombs instead. After they had seen the monuments, the verger offered, for a small fee, to show them the body of Catherine de Valois. The body was in its plain wooden box behind the altar and had become 'as leather', with mobile limbs. Pepys writes that he took the opportunity to take the lady in his arms and kiss her, so that he had 'this day kissed a queen'. Catherine remained in this position until 1793, when she was again placed in the plain tomb she now occupies.

Catherine's husband, Owen ap Meredyth ap Tudor, also has no tomb. He was captured after the Battle of Mortimer's Cross by Edward, Duke of York. He was executed in the market place at Hereford.

Henry VI

~

Born 1421
Murdered Tower of London, 24 May 1471

THERE IS no doubt that Henry VI inherited a degree of mental instability from his mother, Catherine de Valois. Her father, Charles VI of France, had also shown marked mental symptoms. As a youth and in later life, Henry had attacks of melancholy and even a depressive psychosis. His worst attack began on 10 August 1453 and lasted until the Christmas of 1454. A second attack in the autumn of 1455 lasted until February 1456. During the attacks he would sit without moving and pay little attention to what was happening around him. The reports of when his son was born, probably on New Year's Day 1454, seem to be fairly typical. It was felt that the sight of his son might make him improve and bring him out of the severe attack, during which he had sat immobile. But when the Duke of Buckingham presented his son to him, Henry took no notice and spoke no word. As the duke had failed to get a response, 'The Queene came in, and toke the Prince in her armes and presented hym in like forme as the duke had done, desiryng that he shuld blisse it; but alle their labour was in veyne for they departed thens without any answere or countenaunce savyng only that ones he loked on the Prince and caste dounne his eyene ayan, without any more.' This is a tragic picture of Queen Margaret, a most active and powerful woman, trying to get her unfortunate husband to show some love for his son. Indeed, she was to defend her son and fight for his rights all her life.

Henry came to the throne at a very early age on the death of his father Henry V. He was crowned King of England in 1430 and he was the only monarch to be also crowned King of France, in Paris. The early part of his reign was a struggle to retain all the French conquests his father had made, while Joan of Arc was trying to restore the French cause. As he was so young when he ascended the throne it was necessary that there should be a period of regency. This created a power struggle which was to develop throughout his reign and blossom out into the Wars of the Roses.

To follow the events which were finally to lead to his death, we need a brief history of the events of his reign. Henry was descended from John of Gaunt, while the Duke of York was descended from Lionel, Duke of Clarence, an older son of Edward III (See page 74). York was constantly advised to seize the protectorship and even the crown. Margaret, Henry VI's wife, fought throughout her life for the rights of her husband and son and at the Battle of Wakefield, York and his son were killed and the cause of York temporarily destroyed. However, the Battle of Mortimer's Cross followed soon after and York's son, Edward, defeated the Lancastrians, led by Owen Tudor, who was married to the widow of Henry V, Catherine de Valois. Tudor was taken to Hereford, where he was executed. His son Jasper Tudor escaped and was to found the Tudor line.

Margaret advanced towards London and met Warwick and Norfolk, who were holding Henry VI captive. At the Battle of St Albans which followed, Margaret triumphed and managed to recapture her husband. Once again the hapless Henry found himself free for a while.

Warwick fled north to join forces with Edward and together they marched to London. There they proclaimed Edward as king and in 1461 Henry VI was deposed. The terrible Battle of Towton Moor followed, and there were very heavy casualties. Edward triumphed and Margaret fled to France. Henry was once again captured and taken by Warwick to London, where he was detained in the Tower.

Then Edward offended Warwick by marrying Elizabeth Woodville and advancing her family at the expense of his. In the ensuing struggle, Warwick was defeated and had to flee to Calais. Here he arranged for his daughter to marry Henry's son, who was now Prince of Wales. He gathered together an army and returned to England, forcing Edward to flee the country. Warwick then released

Henry from the Tower and once again he was restored to the throne.

But Edward was not to be so easily defeated. With the help of the Duke of Burgundy he returned to England. Gathering together an army, he met the forces of Warwick at the Battle of Barnet where, in a fog, Warwick was killed. At the same time Margaret once again landed in England. Edward quickly attacked her forces before they were able to be reinforced by an army collected by her son Jasper Tudor. Margaret was finally defeated at Tewkesbury, where her son the Prince of Wales was captured. He was taken into the presence of Edward and was murdered. It is often said that Richard, Duke of Gloucester killed him, but there is no evidence to support this.

The York cause had triumphed, and Edward was now free of all opposition – apart from Henry VI, who was in the Tower of London. On 21 May 1471, Edward returned to London and within a few hours Henry VI was dead. There is no doubt that Henry was murdered, but we do not know by whom or by what method. Again, it is often said that Richard, Duke of Gloucester was responsible but this does not seem possible: he was not in London at the time, and anyway, he had a great regard for Henry, having served with him and been a member of his household. And when Edward became King, one of the first things he did was to have Henry brought to London for honourable burial.

It is most likely that Henry was stabbed to death in the Tower by his guards, on the orders of Edward. Murder was nothing new to Edward who, as we have seen, had killed Henry's son when he was captured at the Battle of Tewkesbury. To Edward it was essential that Henry should die to avoid continued conflict.

The body of Henry was embalmed and buried in Chertsey Abbey. In 1484, Richard had the body brought to Windsor, where it was reburied. The tomb was opened for examination on 4 November 1910. *The Times* of 12 November reports as follows:

> ...a rectangular box found inside contained a decayed mass of human bones lying in no definite order, mixed with the rotted remains of some material in which they had been wrapped and some dry rubbish and some adipocere. (This is a material resulting from decayed soft tissue.) The bones were examined by Professor MacAlister of Cambridge University who described them as those of a fairly strong man of forty five to fifty five who

was at least five feet nine inches high. The skull bones were much broken but were small and thin in proportion to the stature. Nearly all the bones of the trunk were present as well as those of both legs and of the left arm. The body had certainly been dismembered when put in the box. It had been previously buried in earth for some time and exhumed, this would account for the present condition. To one piece of the skull was attached some hair of a brown colour which in one place was darker and apparently matted with blood.

Henry was murdered in the Tower of London when aged 50. Although he had a depressive psychosis, his life seems to have been remarkably free from other diseases and he took his repeated imprisonment and troubles very well indeed. He had great support from his wife Margaret up to the time of the murder of his son Edward, Prince of Wales, at Tewkesbury.

Edward IV

❦

Born Rouen, 1441
Died Westminster, 9 April 1483

EDWARD IV was born in Rouen, the eldest surviving son of Richard, Duke of York and his wife, Cecily Neville. Their first son, Henry, had died in infancy. They had no fewer than seven sons, three of whom were to play an important part in history: Edward himself, and his brothers Richard, Duke of Gloucester, and George, Duke of Clarence. Edward was nursed by a certain Anne of Caux, under whose care he was very healthy and grew to great stature. She came with him to England and when he became King, he gave her a pension of £120 a year, an arrangement which Richard III continued after the death of Edward.

Edward spent his youth at Ludlow, where he grew up with the other members of the large family. He had fair hair and grew to a remarkable height for the times in which he lived. Examination of his skeleton has shown that he was some 6 feet 4 inches in height. At the age of ten he was created Earl of March.

The then King, Henry VI, lost most of the French conquests made by his stronger father, Henry V. This led to continued trouble and discontent, which persuaded Richard, Duke of York, to press his claim to the throne. It was agreed that Henry should retain the crown, but that after his death, Edward's father should inherit it. As a result, Edward now stood in line for kingship.

Margaret, Henry's wife, was not prepared to accept this, and it was she who led the Lancastrian cause. In 1460 Richard, Duke of York, left his castle at Sandal near Wakefield with a small force. He was attacked by Lancastrian supporters and Richard was killed. His

son, Edmund, the young Earl of Rutland, was captured and executed with a brutality typical of these terrible times. After the Battle of
Wakefield the young boy of 12 was being taken by his tutor, Sir
Robert Aspall, to a place of safety. As they came to the bridge in
Wakefield, they were stopped by Lord Clifford, who recognised the
youth. 'The son of York,' shouted the brutal Clifford. 'Thy father
slew mine and I will slay thee and all thy kin.' With that he plunged
his dagger into the Edmund's heart. This was the kind of brutality
that was to influence Edward later in his career.

Having lost his father and brother, Edward now took control of
the Yorkist army and at Mortimer's Cross he gained his first victory.
There he saw three suns in the sky and from this time took a golden
sun as his emblem. It was after this battle that Owen Tudor was captured and executed. A further very bloody battle had to be fought at
Towton before Edward was to become king. This battle was the
bloodiest of the Wars of the Roses, with heavy casualties on both
sides. From this time on Edward's character hardened and it is said
of him '…ambition and cruelty were his leading features. Gratitude
and mercy were unknown to him. Of the two noblest feelings of a
ruler, respect for the rights of his subjects and pity for their suffer-
ings, he appears to have been altogether destitute.' The fine young
man became a very hardened soldier. The ruthlessness of his character is shown in 1478 when Edward had no hesitation in having his
own brother Clarence murdered. Clarence was drowned in a butt
of wine for having allied himself with Warwick against Edward.

Edward now became King. Described by the *Croyland Chronicle*
in 1461 as 'a person of most elegant appearance and remarkable
beyond all others for the attraction of his person', he presented a
very different person from Henry VI. He took a most active personal interest in all matters and he appeared in person on the King's
Bench. The healthy King seemed set for a prosperous and peaceful
reign.

But it is at this point of his history that Edward's carefully
arranged career seems to have faltered. His friend, the Earl of
Warwick, decided that an alliance with France would be greatly to
their advantage and so proposed that Edward should marry the
daughter of the King of France's sister, a most eligible young lady.
Warwick had been negotiating with this in view when, in
September 1464, Edward told his council that he could not proceed

with the marriage since he had married a certain Elizabeth Woodville some five months previously. The effect this extraordinary piece of information would have had can be imagined.

According to tradition, Edward first met Elizabeth when he was returning to London after the Battle of Mortimer's Cross, at which Elizabeth's husband had been killed. Edward stayed at Stony Stratford, where Elizabeth lived, for a few days, and it was said that during this time the young widow waylaid Edward while he was out hunting and pleaded with him for the inheritance of her two young sons. This meeting between the beautiful widow and Edward is said to have taken place beside an oak in the forest at Whittlebury. It seems that Edward was not able to persuade her to become his mistress, so he married her in secret, a fact which caused the validity of the marriage to be questioned at a later date by Richard, the King's brother. Elizabeth had two sons and several brothers and sisters, all of whom were ambitious, and who received positions of importance under her influence. This unfortunate marriage caused Warwick to take up arms against his erstwhile friend. Edward was defeated in the fight and forced to leave the country. Warwick restored Henry VI to the throne.

The energetic young Edward made allies on the continent and returned to England, gathering together the forces of York. As we saw, the forces of Warwick were defeated at Barnet and the earl killed. Edward now became the only king of England ever to gain his throne by force of conquest on two occasions. So began the second period of Edward's reign.

We now find that Edward altered in many ways. He started to become corpulent, a change which was to progress as he got older, and he developed a great love for fine clothes and adornment, spending vast sums on clothes, silver and gold plate. He set to work to build a great chapel at Windsor, to be called the Chapel of St George. He was also considerably influenced by the Arthurian legend and started a 'round table', possibly the great round table to be seen at Winchester today. He built many royal residences and collected a fine library.

By 1480, Edward had changed greatly from the healthy and fine young man who first came to the throne. He was now very corpulent indeed, and it is said that his love for food was such that he used an emetic after a banquet so that he could immediately gorge again. His sexual appetite had also not dimmed with age; rather, it appeared to have increased. He now took three mistresses, of whom it was said one was the merriest, the second the wiliest and the third the holiest in the country. Probably the merriest was Jane Shore, the wife of a London grocer. She is described as being of a very attractive appearance, although a little short in height. She must have been a most attractive woman, since Lord Hastings and the Earl of Dorset also courted her favours.

So far as we know, Edward had two illegitimate children. By Elizabeth Lucy, he had a son, called Arthur Plantagenet, who was created Viscount Lisle in 1523 by Henry VII. The second child was a daughter, about whom very little is known, including her name; she appears to have been brought up in the household of Elizabeth Woodville. These love affairs have brought about speculation that Edward contracted venereal disease, but this seems unlikely. He produced two children and neither showed any evidence of the disease; he also had a legitimate daughter who seems to have been healthy.

However, we do begin to notice a change in Edward's health in 1481. At this time he had planned to help his brother Richard in an attack on Scotland. Making vague excuses he failed to do this, the first time that he had failed his faithful brother. Meanwhile he continued to gain weight and became more sedentary. Political affairs bothered him; he was disappointed by the Treaty of Arras, in which Louis of France arranged a marriage between the Dauphin and Mary of Burgundy's daughter. It was a bitter blow to Edward that his ally, Burgundy, made peace with France.

Edward was now not in good health. His obesity prevented exercise and he would move from place to place seeking relief. In March 1483 he made a visit to Windsor, returning to Westminster on the 25th. A few days later he was seized with a violent illness associated with chest pains and prostration. These continued for some five days, becoming more severe. What is quite plain is that none who attended the King understood what was happening to him. There were several theories: that he had been poisoned; that he had caught a cold while out fishing on the Thames; that he had apoplexy brought on by the Treaty of Arras; that he had malaria. As the *Croyland Chronicle* reports, the King was 'neither worn out with old age, nor yet seized with any known kind of malady'.

We can exclude the possibility of venereal infection, since Edward had a chest pain and took several days to die. As he had developed such obesity, a coronary thrombosis is a possibility. That he had contracted a cold while fishing on the Thames seems to be a reasonable explanation. A chest infection could very well have been the cause of his symptoms and such an infection, in one so obese, might well progress to pneumonia. This in turn could lead to pleurisy with chest pain. One also has to consider the possibility that there may have been a complicating factor, such as diabetes, which is apt to develop in the obese. This would further increase the danger of a chest infection. It seems to have been after some five days that Edward finally became unconscious and died. Pneumonia, complicated by pleurisy, is thus a likely cause of death.

As soon as the great King was dead, the body was washed and left lying completely naked for all to see, being merely covered by a loincloth. He lay thus for about 12 hours, after which he was moved to St Stephen's Chapel in Westminster, where he lay for a further eight days. He was probably embalmed, although we have no record of this being done. After a service in Westminster Abbey, he was conveyed to the new and very beautiful tomb in Windsor which he had been building and which was not yet completely finished. He was laid to rest and the officers of the household threw in their staves of office and the heralds their tabards.

Whatever caused his sudden end, Edward had not taken reasonable steps to see that his son ascended the throne without trouble. Inclined to leave matters in the hands of his faithful brother Richard, he may well have thought that his son Edward could rely on Richard's full support. How wrong he was in this surmise soon became only too clear.

Richard III

❧

Born Fotheringay Castle, 2 October 1452
Died in battle Bosworth Field, August 1485

He himself manfully fighting in the midst of his enemies
was slain. (*Holinshed Chronicle*)

R I C H A R D was born the seventh child of the Duke of York and there had been no thought of his ever becoming King. While he was still a child his father had been defeated at the Battle of Wakefield and both his father and his brother Edmund were killed, and their heads spiked and exhibited at York.

The young Richard was placed in the household of the Earl of Warwick and it was there that he attained his skill in warfare. As a child he was somewhat sickly and developed rickets, a disease resulting from a vitamin deficiency. Due to this, his spine developed a curvature, a condition called adolescent scoliosis, which meant it was bent from side to side. This resulted in one of his shoulders being higher than the other, a common enough condition at this time; it did not interfere with his strength and he was an excellent jouster. Nonetheless, he was small in stature and stockily built. As an adult, he found that he was at his best when dealing with military matters and making rapid decisions: he was used by his brother Edward IV on several occasions to act in military matters on his behalf.

To briefly recap the events described in the previous two chapters, Edward had made his bid for the crown knowing that Henry VI had been a poor King who nevertheless had the support of the

House of Lancaster. Edward, as the head of the House of York, had triumphed at Mortimer's Cross and at Towton and now was King. Richard remembered how he had been at these battles where the 'sun in all her glory' had shone for the Yorkists and a bloody victory was theirs. Both sides suffered very heavily and hundreds were slain, a bloody baptism indeed for Richard.

Throughout the turbulent times of the Wars of the Roses, peace was not to come. Edward had married Elizabeth Woodville, which upset Warwick, who rebelled against him. Together, Edward and Richard defeated Warwick, who had to flee abroad. Richard had been made Constable of England for his part in this battle.

Warwick then returned with an army and defeated Edward, who in turn had to flee from the battlefield. Edward went abroad only to return when he had gathered an army, and supported by Richard he defeated Warwick at Barnet and killed the earl. After the battle the body of Warwick was stripped naked and displayed for two days in order to prove that the Kingmaker was indeed dead. On the same day as this battle was fought, Queen Margaret landed in England in support of her son Edward, whom she hoped to make King. He was the only son of Henry VI and the true heir to the throne.

Together Edward and Richard hastened to meet this new threat and at Tewkesbury they triumphed once again. The young Edward was killed. Only Henry VI now stood in the way of a lasting peace, so back to London went Edward IV and his brother Richard. Henry had to die and was killed in his prison in the Tower.

In the time of relative peace after the murder of Henry VI, Richard married Anne, the daughter of Warwick. They had grown up together in the Warwick household. Anne had previously been married to Edward, Prince of Wales, when Warwick had thought that his daughter would become queen. With the murder of Edward, Anne was free to marry Richard and they were a very loving couple – in spite of the opposition from Clarence, Richard's brother, and his wife, an elder sister of Anne.

Family matters were complicated in 1478, when Clarence plotted against his brother Edward, the King, and was found guilty of treason. Although Richard and Clarence were not close, Richard had a deep regard for his brothers and was deeply affected when Clarence was murdered in the Tower. Richard swore to avenge the death. He was convinced that Elizabeth Woodville, the queen, exerted undue influence on her husband and that it was she who persuaded him of the need to kill Clarence. She was worried that on the death of her husband Clarence would seize the throne. As Clarence had a son, Elizabeth thought that her children would be excluded; and so poor Clarence was drowned in a butt of wine.

From this time onward, Richard was very rarely at court, preferring to live with his wife in the north. He spent a considerable time at York where he was very popular indeed. He knew that the Woodville family plotted against him in London, but so long as the King lived he was quite safe. Should his brother die, the situation would change.

Scotland was again a source of trouble and Edward requested that Richard make an attack which he would later come to support. Richard did as requested, but the King never arrived. For the first time it appeared that the Woodvilles had managed to drive a wedge between Richard and his brother. Richard returned from Scotland with his army, secure in his own strength. He was well aware that his brother had changed greatly during the last two years and was now very obese, disinclined to any activity and considerably aged. In the event of his brother's death, Richard would have to act decisively and quickly to eliminate the Woodville menace.

The need to act came with frightening suddenness: Edward died after a very short illness. However, Richard was well prepared. With a strong force he marched south. Fortunately for Richard, the young heir, Prince Edward, who was at Ludlow, took his time in deciding to leave for London. Richard was able to catch him and the Woodvilles, who rode with him, before they had reached Stony Stratford. There all the Woodvilles were executed, while the young King and his brother were imprisoned in the Tower of London and murdered. Richard was now King and Clarence was avenged.

Following this, Lord Hastings, a member of Richard's council who had appeared to be a strong supporter, refused to co-operate with certain of his plans and had to be removed. Invited to a council meeting in the Tower, he was arrested and immediately executed. This affected the other members of the council very deeply and, too late, Richard realised that this had been a great mistake. The council understood that if one as important as Hastings could be

so easily killed, they were equally at risk. There had been no semblance of a trial and the order to execute Hastings came solely from
the King. Stanley, in particular, realised his dangerous position – he
was married to the mother of the Lancastrian contender to the
throne, Henry Tudor. Secret opposition to Richard started to grow.
Even Buckingham, once Richard's greatest supporter, now thought
that Richard was so unpopular that he could easily be displaced.
His attempt was swiftly defeated and he was arrested and executed
– another friend went the way of so many others.

It seemed, though, that peace had come at last. Richard spent his
time at Sheriff Hutton with his small family, his dear wife Anne and
their son, a sickly child who gave them cause for anxiety. Early in
1484 the young boy showed signs of progressive illness: he lost
weight and appetite and then with great suddenness he died.
Richard and Anne were devastated with grief; they were seen walking together, clinging to each other's hand. Anne herself was far
from well and most unlikely to have another child. No sooner had
Richard got over this loss than his dear wife also died. He was now
completely alone.

It was at this time that the exiled Henry Tudor chose to arrive
from France with a small army, and challenge Richard to battle.
The force he brought over consisted of some very inferior troops
and he could easily have been attacked in south Wales before he was
able to gather more forces. This did not happen, though, and
Henry managed to advance almost as far as Leicester, reaching
Bosworth. Here he had to be defeated and it was essential for
Richard that he should also be killed.

On the morning of 22 August 1485, Richard woke from a fitful
sleep. Ever since the death of his son and wife he had had disturbing
dreams. However, as he rode from the Blue Boar at Leicester he was
fully confident that he would win the battle with Henry Tudor, as
he had done on so many previous occasions. His forces had collected during the last three days and he knew that they were excellent
and well tried. With him were the Dukes of Norfolk and
Northumberland, both supported by well-seasoned troops. The
Earl of Stanley had not come to his aid as requested, but his force
was known to be relatively small and to make sure that Stanley did
indeed support his cause Richard held Stanley's son, Lord Strange,
as hostage. Richard knew that the objective of this battle was to

destroy once and for all the attempts of Henry Tudor to take the throne. All were prepared for battle.

What Richard failed to appreciate on this fateful day was that his popularity was at a very low ebb. Although he was the most experienced general of his time and one of the finest in battle, and although many appreciated his firm rule after the terrible times of the Wars of the Roses, he now stood for the 'old times' of unending strife. His elimination of all who stood in his path frightened even his old friends such as Northumberland. On the day of this battle he therefore stood very much alone. Feared he might be, but he would struggle to hold his party together against Henry, who had agreed to marry Elizabeth, the daughter of Edward IV, and so unite the Houses of York and Lancaster to bring peace.

When the first stage of the battle took place, the centres clashed, and in the mêlée the Duke of Norfolk was killed. His son, Surrey, extricated himself but it was a minor reverse. The battle progressed, with Richard making a most unusual decision. Observing that it would be possible to pass the right flank of Henry's army and attack Henry himself, he sent out scouts to make sure of where Henry Tudor stood. He was told that there was no doubt that he stood near his standard; if Henry could be killed, the battle was as good as won. The right flank of Henry's army was to some extent covered by Stanley. Stanley led a force of some 2,000 men, who stood over to the right of the battle, so far uncommitted to either side. Any move to attack Henry might prompt Stanley into coming to his aid. Therefore the part played by Northumberland would be crucial to the outcome: he was holding himself in readiness to counter-attack if Stanley moved in support of Henry.

Richard therefore decided to attack, covered by Northumberland and using his bodyguard, which did not usually commit itself to battle. Its priority was the protection of the King, to ensure that if the battle were to go against him he could leave the field in safety and live to fight another day. To use such a force in general battle was most unusual and may be taken as evidence of Richard's desperation to kill Henry. With this hand-picked force of some 120 men, Richard rode down the hill with Stanley on his flank. With him rode his faithful Constable of the Tower, his friends Sir Robert Percy and Francis, Viscount Lovell, and even his secretary, John Kendall, put on full armour and rode with him. Richard was off to seek out Henry Tudor and achieve an instant victory.

However, he was well aware that Stanley's men could take on his small force, and probably with fatal impact. That he did not trust Stanley is obvious – just before he set off he gave an order for Lord Strange to be killed. Those in charge held their hands, waiting for the outcome of both this desperate charge and the battle. It was obvious to many that the attack was a great hazard. William Catesby is said to have strongly advised against such an attack and did not himself engage, only to be killed later.

With his squires and household, Richard swung round the battle line to the right and passed across the front occupied by Stanley. His safety now depended entirely on Northumberland. Stanley's force was mostly cavalry and could move with rapidity, a fact of which Richard was well aware. Richard rode straight for the ranks of Henry Tudor's guard and standard. As he did so, the large figure of the famous knight Sir John Cheyney blocked his path. With his battleaxe, Richard struck him down. He was winning a path straight at Henry, who must have found it a dreadful moment as the small force drove at him and his standard. Henry dared not flee, lest it cause his force to lose heart. Richard then reached the standard held by William Brandon: the dragon of Wales. He struck him down and now had only a few yards to go.

At this vital moment, the force accompanying Richard had to turn to the right to defend their King. A large mass of men, the main body of horse commanded by Sir William Stanley, were attacking their flank. The King's small defending force was overwhelmed. Meanwhile, Northumberland did not move, but watched the battle without engaging his forces: he had turned traitor and it was he who was responsible for what was to follow. This fact was appreciated by Richard's followers who were to murder Northumberland three years later.

Richard was now unprotected by his household and had to fight on alone. Many weapons smashed against his armour and his helmet with its circle of gold fell from his head. Crying 'Treason, treason' to Northumberland, who had left him to his fate, he fell lifeless to the ground. There he was stripped of his armour, just as Warwick had been stripped after the Battle of Barnet. The main battle came to a halt and still Northumberland sat immobile. Sir William Stanley's party found the gold circlet from Richard's head and he, or possibly his brother, placed it on the head of Henry Tudor. (This did not prevent Henry from executing him some years later.)

The naked body of Richard was flung across a horse. One of his heralds was forced to ride the horse and the corpse was borne back towards Leicester. It was then left exposed in the house of the Grey Friars, close to the river, for the usual two days so that all might view him. Finally, it was placed in an unmarked grave.

Some years later, Henry VII gave a sum of ten pounds and one shilling for the cost of a tomb for Richard. At the dissolution of the monasteries, the Grey Friars was plundered and Richard's tomb destroyed. It is said that his body was thrown into the river.

Richard is the only King of England to have been killed in battle and the only king to have no known grave.

Henry VII

~

Born Pembroke Castle, 1457
Died Richmond, 21 April 1509

WHEN HE WAS born, Henry did not appear to be a child destined to become a king. Henry's grandfather, Owen Tudor, had worked in the household of Catherine de Valois, the widow of Henry V. They fell in love and probably married in 1425. They had five children, two of whom, Edmund and Jasper, were to play a significant part in the life of Henry VII. Edmund Tudor married Margaret Beaufort, the great-granddaughter of John of Gaunt, and it was through this connection that Henry claimed a right to the throne.

His mother, Lady Margaret Beaufort, had been very young indeed when she married. While she was pregnant, her husband Edmund Tudor was sent to take control of south Wales during the Wars of the Roses. He was captured by Yorkists and imprisoned in Carmarthen Castle, where he died aged 26. In later years, Henry was to honour the memory of his father by having his remains moved from Grey Friars in Carmarthen to St David's Cathedral. Lady Beaufort was protected by her brother-in-law, Jasper Tudor, Earl of Pembroke, who took her to his castle. There, after she had been a widow for 12 weeks, she gave birth to Henry in one of the tower chambers.

Margaret and her child were still living in Pembroke Castle when Edward IV seized the throne. The castle was captured and Jasper had to flee. Henry was placed under the excellent guardianship of William Herbert, and even became betrothed to Herbert's daughter. However, when Henry was only 12 years old, Richard Neville,

Earl of Warwick, declared Herbert a traitor and he was executed. The next year, Warwick restored Henry VI to the throne and the fortunes of the Tudors improved. The King actually saw his young nephew from Wales when Jasper, restored to favour, brought him to court.

At this time, Henry seems to have been in reasonable health. He is said to have been slender, but well built and strong, his height being above the average. His eyes were small and blue and his hair was dark but became white with age; it was always thin and became much more so as he aged. He rode well, but did not have a great liking for military matters.

Jasper was later involved in the Battle of Tewkesbury, where the Lancastrians were defeated. To avoid capture, Jasper and his 14-year-old nephew made for the coast. They were nearly caught at Chepstow, but managed to reach Tenby and finally the sanctuary of St Malo, where they were given asylum by the Duke of Brittany.

Henry was to be in exile for 14 years. While abroad, he fathered a healthy child named Roland de Velville by a young Breton girl. This child was never to press the claims of his parenthood; in later life he was, however, knighted by his father and became constable of Beaumaris Castle in Anglesey.

His mother, Margaret Beaufort, also had her troubles. In the year of her son's escape to Brittany, her second husband, Sir Henry Stafford, died. Two years later, she married Thomas, Lord Stanley, who was a Yorkist and supporter of Edward IV, but had changed sides at Bosworth.

With the death of Henry VI and his son's murder at Tewkesbury, the future Henry VII became the head of the House of Lancaster and as such posed a threat to Edward IV. The Duke of Brittany was pressed to surrender his young 'guest'. This he refused to do. Henry made every effort to see that he was not sent back to England and even feigned fever.

The first real opportunity for Henry to return came with the revolution organised by the Duke of Buckingham. Buckingham had once been a great supporter of Richard III, but tired of his tyrannical behaviour. Though well planned, his rising was premature and alerted Richard. Buckingham was prevented from joining his forces by a flood of the River Severn and he was captured in

Shropshire. Henry, meanwhile, had sailed from Brittany with the intention of supporting Buckingham, but had not landed owing to the bad weather. He was to have arrived at Poole, but sailed west to Plymouth, where he was invited to land. Fearing a trap and hearing of the failure of the rising, he returned to Brittany; he had been very lucky indeed. He now swore an oath that if he were to be King of England, he would marry Elizabeth of York and unite the two houses of York and Lancaster.

In 1485, Henry again made a crossing with a small army and landed at Milford Haven. It was essentially a Welsh operation and Henry got considerable local support. His forces eventually met Richard at Market Bosworth, where, due to the treachery of Northumberland and Stanley, he triumphed. Henry took no active part in the battle.

His coronation had to be postponed due to the appearance amongst the population of a strange plague called the 'sweating sickness'. This peculiar disease was also called the 'Sudor Anglicus', which suggests that it was confined to England, where it broke out on four occasions between 1485 and 1551. It was characterised by the very rapid onset of a high fever with possible delirium; either death followed in a few hours or the patient recovered with severe upset and great weakness. It has been suggested that it was a severe strain of influenza. Henry and his family were very fortunate in that they appear to have completely escaped the disease.

Early in the reign came a lawsuit concerning the body of Henry VI, who was now looked upon with great reverence. The monks of Westminster claimed a right to the body, which was contested by the ecclesiastical authorities of Windsor and Chertsey. Westminster prevailed and permission was obtained from Pope Julius II to remove the body from Chertsey to Westminster. The idea of canonisation was very seriously considered, which would have resulted in a king of England becoming a saint. Henry eventually gave up the idea because of the very large sums demanded by the papal court to give the matter due consideration.

Henry VII's plan to build a new and magnificent chapel was originally conceived in order to honour Henry VI. It was also to be the resting place for himself so that he might be buried 'along with his uncle'. Much of the money raised for the Henry VII Chapel at the Abbey was intended for a chapel to Henry VI.

On becoming King, Henry married Elizabeth of York. The couple had three sons and two daughters, but the health of the family was not very good. Henry's eldest son, Arthur, was sent to Ludlow to learn the elements of government and be groomed for the crown. Henry placed all his aspirations on Arthur, who unfortunately developed what was probably pulmonary tuberculosis. He was a very well-built youth, but shortly before his marriage to Catherine of Aragon, he developed a recurrent fever, most probably an exacerbation of his chest infection. (It is also likely that Henry himself had mild progressive pulmonary tuberculosis.) Arthur's condition deteriorated rapidly and he died, which led to some debate as to whether he had consummated his marriage.

The death of Arthur was a terrible blow to the King, but he still had a male heir in Prince Henry, who had been intended for the Church. Aged 11 at this time, he was created Prince of Wales and seemed to be a very healthy child. However, the high infant mortality of the times was always a great threat to the succession. The King's third child was a daughter, Elizabeth, who died in 1495; five years later his fourth child, Prince Edmund, also died. There was still the possibility of another child as Elizabeth had become pregnant once again, but she was unwell during most of the pregnancy. The child was born in the Tower of London, in the upper floor of the White Tower. The delivery produced yet another girl, who was christened Catherine. A week after the birth, the weakened queen died and, a few days later, so did the little Catherine. Henry had now lost his wife and four of his children.

There are two major reasons for the high mortality associated with childbearing throughout the Middle Ages. Apart from the possibility of infection being produced by the actual birth, the frequency of the pregnancies was an obvious danger. Women of the time had an abnormal iron metabolism due to a diet consisting mainly of grain and vegetables supplemented by sweet food such as honey. The women did not eat as much meat as the men did, and their iron intake would be in the range of 0.25–0.75 mg per day. While this would be sufficient to maintain reasonable metabolism in men, it was quite inadequate in menstruating women, since iron is essential for the proper formation of blood. Without an adequate intake of iron, anaemia follows, as the red blood cells are deficient in the oxygen-carrying material haemoglobin. If we assume that a woman had an intake of 0.75 mg per day, she would lose iron progressively when she started to menstruate, as her annual intake of 275 mg would prove inadequate by some 200 mg. If she started with a store of 1925 mg at the age of 14, she would have lost so much iron by the age of 23 as to be severely anaemic. Pregnancy would be a severe strain, both to her and to the foetus; second and third pregnancies might seriously imperil life. Also, with this degree of anaemia, a woman would be very prone to intercurrent infection, as her resistance would be so low. Thus we find both maternal and child deaths common at this time. The method of bleeding as a treatment for illness would naturally increase the liability for mortality.

From 1497 Henry's own health began to deteriorate, although he had taken great care of himself. In order to guard his son Henry, he isolated the child and limited access to a few chosen persons. He now found that his own vision was failing, and since he took a great personal interest in all accounts and state papers, he was worried that he might lose contact with these matters. He tried various eye lotions and eyebaths, made of fennel-water, rose-water and celandine, 'to make bright the sight', but to no avail. He was also slowly losing weight, although his appetite remained reasonable. His teeth were a source of trouble and we find Polydore Vergil describing him as having 'teeth few, poor and blackish'. Henry was definitely showing the onset of old age, although he was only 50 years old.

He also developed a chronic cough which was particularly severe in springtime. The condition became progressively more severe and was associated with loss of weight and a general wasting. In 1507 and 1508 his spring cough became most troublesome. He is described as having become troubled with a tissic, or cough. He also suffered from mild gout.

In his life of Henry VII, Bacon writes: 'In the two and twentieth year of his reign in 1507, he began to be troubled with a gout, but the defluxation taking also unto his breast wasted his lungs, so that thrice in a year (in a kind of return and especially in the spring) he had great fits, and labours of the tissick.' This suggests that Henry suffered from chronic fibroid phthisis (chronic tuberculous infection), which became more and more active with resultant wasting and debility. This infection is found in several of the members of the Tudor line.

Henry made a great effort to attend divine service on Easter Day 1509, but he was exhausted and retired to his palace at Richmond. On 21 April he died from chronic pulmonary tuberculosis. He is said to have called his son Henry to his bedside and extracted from him a promise that he would marry Catherine of Aragon.

> This year 1509, The king began to be diseased of a certain infirmity which thrice a year, but espoecially in the spring time sore vexed him. The sickness which held the king daily more and more increasing he well perceived that his end drew near. He was so wasted with his long malady that nature could no longer sustain his life, and so he departed out of this world the two and twentieth of April. (*Holinshed Chronicle*)

In his will, the reason for his burial at Westminster is stated:

> Ane forasmuche as we have received our solempne coronation and holie Inunction within our Monasterie of Westminster, and that within the same monasterie is the common sepulture of the Kings of this Raems; and Sp'cially because that within the same and wmong the same Kings rseteth the holie bodye and reliquiers of the Gloriuos King the Confessor, Saint Edward, and diverse others of the noble progenitours and blood, and specially the body of our Great dame memorie, Quene Kateryne, wif to King Henry the Vth, and daughter of Charles of France, and that we by the grace of God P'pose right shortly to translate into the same the body and reliquiers of our uncle of blessed memorye, King Henry VIth. For thies and divers other causes and considerations us sp'ially moevyng in that behalf we wol that whensoever it shall please our Savious Jn'u Crist to calle us oute of this transitorie lif, be it within this our Reyme [realm], or in any other Reyme or place withoute the same, that our bodie be buried within the same monasterie; that is to saie, in the chapell where our said graunt Damr laye buried, the which chapell, we have begonne to buylde of newe in the honour of our blessed Lady.

In spite of the stress laid on the 'Great Dame', the coffin of Catherine de Valois, wife of Henry V, was treated with little respect. It was disinterred from its place in front of the high altar and

Catherine's body was left in its simple coffin behind the same altar for some 200 years before she was finally laid to rest. Most probably Henry VIII was the person responsible for this dishonour.

Henry VIII

⁓

Born 28 June 1491
Died Westminster, 27 January 1547

Our King, having laboured under the burden of extreme fat and unwieldy body, and together being afflicted with a sore leg, took, at the Palace of Westminster in January this year, his death bed; being for the rest not without sense of his present condition. At the last, he desired to speak with Cranmer, who not yet coming sooner than the King was speechless, though in good memory, the King extended his hand to him. (From the *Life of Herbert of Cherbury*)

Henry, long since grown corpulent, was becoming a burden to himself and of late lame by reason of a violent ulcer in his leg, the inflammation wereof cast him into a lingering fever which, little by little, decayed his spirits. He at length began to feel the inevitable necessity of death. (Goodwin Annales of England)

T H O S E   W H O wrote about the King's health had to be careful as it was considered treasonable to speculate. Descriptions of his last illness thus tend to be wildly optimistic. More recently, historians have found Henry's medical history to be of great interest and there has been more written about him than about any other King: many papers have been given at the Royal College of Surgeons and elsewhere. Most opinions of his various illnesses have, however, been somewhat biased in that conclusions have been formed about the nature of Henry's troubles and the facts then fitted to support these theories. This is particularly noticeable in regard to the possibility of his having syphilis. A brief history of the events of his life might be of some help.

Henry was born on 28 June 1491, the second son of Henry VII and Elizabeth of York, who died nine years later. A healthy child, he appears to have been secondary to his elder brother, Arthur, who received most of the attention of his loving father. As a child Henry attended various functions, usually in support of his elder brother. However, Arthur died of pulmonary tuberculosis, the same disease which later killed their father. Perhaps as a result, the young Henry was closely guarded by his father from excessive personal contact with other people to prevent the possibility of contacting a communicable disease. Henry continued in good health, with no evidence of having intercurrent infection. Well-built and strong, he was an excellent tennis player, an accomplished jouster and a formidable wrestler. He rode well and could tire out three horses in one day, and his friends found difficulty in equalling his energy. He had an attractive and pleasant personality as a youth, but did not make friends easily, and we have no record of any real friendships other than those with his brother-in-law, Brandon, and possibly Cranmer. He was intelligent, a good scholar and a linguist. Also deeply religious, he had an excellent knowledge of the scriptures; before the death of his brother Arthur, he may have been destined for the Church. As a young man, he had a good head of hair and he grew a beard in early adult life.

In 1501, his elder brother, Arthur, married the Spanish princess Catherine of Aragon, but became ill very shortly afterwards and was to die within a few months. He had progressive pulmonary tuberculosis, but does not appear to have passed on his disease to his wife. There are varying reports as to whether he consummated his marriage, but it seems that Henry believed that Catherine was a virgin when he later married her, having obtained a papal dispensation to do so. Catherine had a difficult widowhood since her father-in-law, Henry VII, gave her little money; considering her status, she lived in some degree of poverty. In 1507, she developed a questionable relationship with a dissolute Franciscan monk, her Spanish confessor. This monk, Diego Fernandez, was a very domineering man of low moral standard. He developed great power over Catherine, who appears to have been fascinated by him – so much so that she retained him in her household for several years and refused to give him up. The Spanish ambassador reported the matter to Catherine's father in Madrid, without indicating how far the relationship had gone. Finally Diego was convicted of fornication and dismissed from his office. This strange relationship poses the first of many difficulties in a medical consideration of Catherine's history. Her ability to bear children was severely compromised, perhaps because sexual contact with a promiscuous priest led to her contracting syphilis. This she could have passed on to her future husband. Possibly, therefore, it was she, rather than Henry, who was the cause of her many miscarriages.

In April 1509 Henry VII died and Henry VIII came to the throne. He was 18 years old and there was great rejoicing that a young and attractive man was to replace the aged and parsimonious old King. Events moved swiftly. Henry was proclaimed King on 22 April, married to Catherine on 3 June, and the couple were crowned on 24 June. In doing this, Henry VIII was following the advice of his father who had made him promise that he would marry Catherine.

We have no knowledge of Henry having had any sexual experiences before his marriage, although since he was a very 'active and strong' prince it seems unlikely that he had no experience at all. Catherine became pregnant immediately after her marriage and gave birth to a stillborn daughter on 31 January 1510, seven and a half months later; presumably it was a premature birth. Just a few months later, Henry was carrying on a flirtation with a sister of the Duke of Buckingham who, sensing the danger, removed the lady from court. On 1 January 1511 Catherine gave birth to a fully developed boy, who was baptised Henry. Unfortunately he was a very sickly child and died when he was just 52 days old. The cause of his sickness and death is not known. This was obviously a great blow to Henry, but he was confident that he could have more children and, in the knowledge that Catherine was again pregnant, he was away in France from June to October 1513. However, in September 1513 Catherine had a further miscarriage.

Then in January 1514, three months after his return from France, Henry developed a curious skin disease, which was to last for two months. It intrigued him greatly, since he took a detailed interest in medical matters. His rash was treated by many applications, some suggested by Henry himself. It affected most of his body, but did not influence his general health in any way, and disappeared within two months, leaving no scarring.

This rash could have been a secondary syphilitic rash, which characteristically disappears after about two months and affects most of the body. Syphilis passes through three stages, the first of which is a sore or chancre, which usually develops on the genitals. This then heals and is followed by a secondary stage, where there is usually a generalised rash. The third stage is where the infection attacks many internal organs and frequently the nervous system: areas of the body are destroyed and become white necrotic patches called gummata which, if they occur under the skin, cause ulcers which do not heal. Later in life, Henry was to develop an ulcer on his leg which would not heal in spite of prolonged treatment and this might have been a syphilitic ulcer due to an underlying gumma. There is also a place on one side of Henry's nose, shown in several portraits, which is said to be due to syphilis. Evidence to support the possibility that he had this disease is the fact that syphilis can attack the foetus and cause miscarriage; this may explain what happened to Catherine. Children born of syphilitic parents usually show signs of congenital disease and the sufferers develop progressive nervous and mental symptoms, sometimes terminating in dementia.

This is the disease which Henry might have contracted and which could explain some of the happenings in his reign. The above is in support of his having syphilis, but we find, however, that there are many points in Henry's further medical history which strongly contradict a diagnosis of syphilis.

Henry now had a relationship with a young woman, Elizabeth Blount, who is something of an unknown character; little is written about her. There is no doubt that Henry got on well with her, for they were to continue their relationship for no less than six years, during which Henry also continued a normal relationship with his wife. Elizabeth seems to have been a very easy-going person and never attempted any personal gain from the King. If Henry did have syphilis, he would surely have passed the disease to Elizabeth Blount but there is no evidence that he did so.

In November 1514, Catherine once again had a miscarriage, but was shortly afterwards pregnant once again. This time she was delivered of a live girl on 11 February 1516; the child was christened Mary. This infant was never particularly healthy, but there is no evidence of any congenital syphilis and she remained in reasonable health. In November 1518, Catherine had yet another still birth and from this date it appears that Henry did not cohabit with her, having apparently decided that she was not going to bear him a son.

In 1519, Elizabeth Blount gave birth to a very healthy boy, who was christened Henry Fitzroy. This was a great joy to his father, who now understood that he could have sons by women other than his wife, knowledge which was to strain the relationship between himself and Catherine. Henry Fitzroy continued in good health, there again being no evidence of congenital syphilis. His mother also remained well.

In 1521, it was reported that Henry had an attack of malaria, a disease which was much more prevalent in the Middle Ages than it is today. Malaria is either a tertian fever, occurring every three days, and being moderately severe, or a quartan fever, occurring every four days and being relatively mild. Henry had a quartan fever, which was to affect him at various intervals throughout his life, although it did not greatly incapacitate him.

Henry now became attached to Mary Boleyn, the elder sister of Anne, who at this time was in France. Mary Boleyn was undoubtedly Henry's mistress and she continued in normal health with no evidence of syphilis. She received several costly presents from Henry, but he made no steps to advance her status, determined perhaps to keep his sex life free from political complications.

To judge from his activities, Henry was in excellent health. He took strenuous exercise and indulged in many jousts and tournaments, both on foot and on horse. He had a number of accidents, none serious. In June 1520, Henry was at the Field of the Cloth of Gold, where there were two weeks of dancing, jousting and singing. One day, when it was too windy for jousting, Henry wrestled with the French King, Francis. At one point he took him by surprise, but Francis quickly responded and threw Henry 'flat on his broad back', which must have surprised him greatly. He was later to have two lucky escapes. In March 1524, he was jousting with his usual opponent, the Duke of Suffolk, his brother-in-law. Henry forgot to lower his visor and the crowd, seeing the danger, shouted. Henry thought that they were cheering him on and he charged even harder. Suffolk's lance was shattered on his helm and Henry was very lucky not to have been blinded or even killed. In 1525, at Hitchin Common, he tried to vault a very wide ditch, using a pole, but the pole broke. He was thrown headfirst into the mud of the ditch and was unable either to get up or to breathe. He might well have suffocated but for his footman who rescued him 'or he had drowned'. Henry was an expert at the joust, both on foot and on horse, and there are many pieces of his armour in the Tower collection (now in Leeds). He was also an expert with the bow. In the wreck of the *Mary Rose*, several longbows were found with a pull of 160 pounds, and it is quite possible that Henry could pull such a bow.

The son of Elizabeth Blount was now made Duke of Richmond and Somerset and it seems that Henry was about to declare this attractive young man, of whom he was very fond, heir apparent. But events in Henry's life were to move quickly. He had begun to cast doubts on the validity of his marriage to Catherine. As he was thinking of having his daughter, Mary, married to the French Dauphin, he found that these doubts rebounded: the French King was not anxious to have his son married to a woman who might be declared illegitimate. Henry also thought that the number of stillbirths was a punishment from God for having married the wife of his brother; he therefore petitioned for a divorce from Catherine.

It has to be said that his religious concerns corresponded with the time that he met Anne Boleyn, with whom he appeared to be genuinely in love. Anne proved to be no easy partner, but he was determined to let nothing prevent him from his desires. Anne had been betrothed to the young Percy of the Northumberland family, who was ordered to leave the court and to renounce her, which he did under duress. Anne, however, still resisted Henry's advances, hoping for marriage rather than a casual relationship like that enjoyed by her sister. In August 1532, however, Anne finally became his mistress. Henry desperately needed a son and, after she confided in him that she was pregnant, he married her in January 1533, so that the child might be born legitimate. Her position was ratified by Parliament, but the marriage precipitated the break with Rome, with Henry assuming the position of supreme head of the Church of England.

Confident that the unborn child was going to be a male, he made all preparations for the birth of a son. If Anne had given birth to a son, her history would no doubt have been very different, but on 7 September 1533 she gave birth, with some difficulty, to a healthy daughter, Elizabeth. Henry was bitterly disappointed and from this date appears to have tired of Anne. He took another mistress, Margaret Shelton. In defence, Anne feigned another pregnancy, but this was soon disproved. It is, of course, possible that she attempted to become pregnant by others, as was submitted at her trial, and that she did become pregnant, but had an early miscarriage.

We are now presented with two points of medical interest. Henry received a severe head injury, which Anne claimed caused her to miscarry from worry. The injury might account for the development of symptoms of a mental nature which became more evident from this time onwards. The second point is that Anne had two miscarriages in a short time, evidence perhaps of syphilis. Against this possibility is the fact that the child Elizabeth was in reasonable health, with no trace of disease, as was Anne Boleyn.

Henry, however, had altered in appearance and a fairly rapid change took place following the execution of Anne in 1536. He put on considerable weight and his face became moonlike, burying his small eyes in a puffy face and accentuating his small mouth. He had always been a hard drinker and a glutton, and these characteristics became more marked. By 1537 these symptoms were associated with fits of temper and instability. His great increase in weight made it difficult for him to take any exercise, although he was still capable of riding considerable distances.

Henry also developed an ulcer on his leg. The history of this ulcer is vague and we are not really sure which leg was afflicted, although it seems that it may well have been the left leg. Portraits do not show any alteration in either leg, or evidence of bandaging or swelling, perhaps because the painters sought to please. The ulcer gave Henry considerable trouble and was to do so for the rest of his life. We do know that it appeared to heal over and that he then developed a fever with associated pain; once it opened again, he got relief. Some have speculated that this was a gumma of the leg, but gummata are not painful and they do not heal over with the development of fever. Nor are they offensive, whereas Henry's ulcer was very offensive and a great trial to his attendants. This suggests a common varicose ulcer, which is offensive and is often associated with swelling of the leg, which we know did develop to a marked degree in Henry's later life. A varicose ulcer is sometimes associated with thrombosis of the deep veins, a condition frequently caused by trauma to the leg, and this Henry may well have received during a joust.

A further possibility is that Henry received an injury to the leg which damaged the underlying bone leading to a bone infection, or osteitis. This chronic osteitis would be tender and painful and if the area was to heal over, with the underlying bone infection persisting, then there would be fever and general upset such as we know did occur. All the associated symptoms would thus fit in with osteitis of the tibia with overlying sinus formation, described as 'an ulcerated leg'. This is the most likely explanation of the condition. Chronic infection of this type leads to another complication caused by the chronic poisoning occasioned: amyloid disease, in which a waxy material is laid down in the liver, kidneys and elsewhere. It is thus quite possible that Henry had osteitis associated with amyloid disease.

Jane Seymour, whom Henry now married, was a gentle person who took affectionate care of his two daughters. She must have found the King a great trial, for within one week of her marriage he was expressing regret that he had not met a certain beautiful young girl before his marriage. Mary, Elizabeth and of course Henry Fitzroy were all considered illegitimate. Parliament passed an act giving to Henry the absolute right to pass on his crown as he thought fit, regardless of sex or descent. It is surprising now to realise that Parliament was quite happy at that time to do whatsoever the King wished.

Henry Fitzroy became ill, most probably from the family complaint of pulmonary tuberculosis. He died, leaving Henry with no male descendant. Fortunately, in October 1537 Jane Seymour was delivered of a male child, the future Edward VI. Unfortunately, though, she contracted a mild puerperal sepsis which lay latent for some 12 days, but then flared up. She died 12 days after the birth of her son. Henry had at last produced a reasonably fit male child with no evidence of any possible syphilis. It is most unlikely therefore, that Henry could have been suffering from syphilis at this time.

For political reasons, Henry was now betrothed to a princess of northern Germany and, on the evidence of a miniature painting, he married Anne of Cleves in 1540. She was plain, angular and pockmarked, with little or no knowledge of English. Henry felt unable to consummate the marriage and Anne was sent into retirement with a pension. Henry had in fact now fallen in love with a lady-in-waiting, Catherine Howard, a niece of the Duke of Norfolk, and a girl of 17.

Henry became subject to violent attacks of temper and periods of loss of memory. On leaving London on one occasion he ordered all prisoners in the Tower to be executed. Religious persecutions under the 'six articles' became widespread, with political executions and riots. His character had become most unstable.

In November 1541, his council wished to be rid of Catherine Howard and proceedings against her were taken, disclosing the affairs she was alleged to have had before she was married to Henry. In February 1542, she and all those implicated were executed. It is by no means certain that Henry had even consummated this marriage. Later that year, Henry married the widow of Lord Latimer, Catherine Parr. She remained his wife, with some periods of stress, until his death.

By 1546, Henry had become gross and suffered from violent fits of temper and longer periods of senile feebleness. His legs became so swollen that he was unable to walk, and he was moved from place to place by means of a lifting apparatus. His sight now became very poor, making reading impossible, although his hearing remained reasonable. His feeding habits alternated between periods of excess and periods of loss of appetite. There is no evidence of any vomiting and he does not appear to have had any difficulty in passing urine. In September 1546 it appeared as if he would die; but he made a sudden recovery. In December, he dictated his will, passing the throne to Edward, to be followed by Mary and Elizabeth. There is no evidence of any real mental impairment at this time. Indeed, he was soon to show that he was not incapable. Surrey, the son of Norfolk, appeared to be plotting to seize the crown. With great energy Henry had him arrested and executed and the father, the aged Duke of Norfolk, would also have lost his life had Henry not died before the warrant could be signed.

Towards the end of January 1547, Henry started having periods of partial unconsciousness, alternating with periods of mental alertness; he was probably passing into a uraemic coma. On the 27th, he realised that he was near to death and he asked for Thomas Cranmer. His attendants had obviously not been prepared for his death, or Cranmer would have been readily available. As it was, there was some delay in alerting the archbishop and by the time he arrived, Henry had lost the power of speech. Henry grasped the hand of the archbishop and, when asked if he really did repent of all his sins, pressed it. This was taken as Henry's repentance and so he died 'in grace'.

Henry had died in his own bed. His son and daughter Elizabeth were told of his death on 28 January and both were genuinely most upset with grief. The huge and offensive body was laid to rest in state and placed, with some difficulty, in his coffin, so that he might be buried in Windsor next to his queen, Jane Seymour. The service of committal was interrupted when his coffin burst forth offensive matter and filled the church with a most obnoxious odour.

Certain points in Henry's medical history demand further consideration. The possibility that he had syphilis had been considered by many writers. In 1920, C. Maclaurin decided that the King had indeed had the disease. Dr Kemble, in 1921, agreed, but in 1932, Dr Chamberlain disagreed, pointing out that Henry had never been given mercury as a treatment, although it was then established as the treatment for syphilis. If his doctors had thought that he had the disease, they would undoubtedly have given this remedy. L.H. Appleby, in 1934, thought syphilis likely, but there is no definite proof that the King had this disease and he had extramarital relationships with three women – Elizabeth Blount, Margaret Skelton and Mary Boleyn – none of whom had syphilis. None of his wives showed evidence of the disease and none of his children showed any evidence of congenital syphilis. There are therefore more likely explanations of his symptoms than venereal disease.

We have seen that the ulcer of the legs was probably due to underlying osteitis. His inability to walk in the last two years of his life would have been due to the severe oedema of his legs, associated with his incurable long-standing ulcer and his gross overweight. An endocrine abnormality might well be responsible for his altered appearance, his mental changes and his weight increase.

Much has been made of the abnormality on the side of his nose, which is shown as a swelling in some portraits and as a depression in others. This is taken to indicate that he had a gumma on the right side of his nasal septum and that it had healed with scarring. The portraits and drawings do show such an abnormality, but their evidence is inconclusive.

There are a number of letters written by Henry, which might be thought to show evidence of cerebral abnormality and so possibly be the result of third-stage syphilis. A letter of 1518, written to Cardinal Wolsey, is easily read and correctly punctuated; a second letter of 1544 also shows that the writer suffered from no mental abnormality. However, letters between these dates do show an absence of punctuation and are confused and jumbled. Whether these can be taken to show evidence of progressive mental deterioration such as might result from syphilitic infection is unclear; rather, they provide an insight into Henry's confused mental state.

A summary of points in his medical history show that at 22 he had a skin disease of unknown type, followed in 1514 by a mild attack of smallpox. At 33 he had malaria and at 37 recurrent and severe headaches. He received multiple injuries at the joust, including one of a severe nature, with a loss of consciousness lasting some time. During the last 17 years of his life, he showed marked alteration of his character, associated with progressive obesity. He had a deformity of the nose and a leg ulcer which did not heal. There was a progressive alteration in his psychological make-up, with increased egotism and forgetfulness.

Looking at the many portraits of Henry, he shows such marked alteration that one must consider the possibility of his having had an endocrine abnormality. Lack of thyroid function, or hypothyroidism, would produce the facial configuration, obesity, altered mental make-up and loss of hair, and several of the portraits suggest such a diagnosis. However, those suffering from this abnormality show loss of energy and an inability to undergo physical exertion, which do not seem to have affected Henry initially. His endocrine abnormality, though severe, must have been due to more than simple loss of thyroid function.

Pituitary abnormality, such as a tumour known as basophil adenoma of the pituitary, may be associated with an abnormality of the suprarenal glands, which lie just above the kidney. This abnormality takes the form of enlargement and hyper-function of these glands and produces a mixed clinical picture. The patient alters greatly in appearance, becoming obese with a face which may well be most frightening. He may well become markedly aggressive and quarrelsome with recurrent headaches. Virilism may be found, which is often associated with loss of sexual function, conditions which may well have troubled Henry. Many of these features are found, particularly in his later life, where apparent attraction to many women is associated with an inability to have satisfactory sexual function.

It may well be, therefore, that Henry showed mixed but very definite endocrine abnormality. Mixed abnormality of thyroid, pituitary and suprarenal glands would and probably did produce the progressively unattractive and somewhat terrible picture that we see developing. A very attractive youth changes in later life into something of an ogre, with no friends and only his own aggressive personality and natural cunning to take him through his final years. It makes a very sad picture.

History remembers him as the King who had six wives and suppressed the monasteries. But Henry is to be pitied as a man who had no friends, always sought to achieve what he was incapable of doing, and had a progressive and terrible physical abnormality rendering him obese, unattractive and even repellent.

Henry VIII died from obesity with renal and hepatic failure. It does not appear that he had syphilis, but rather suffered from what might be termed 'Cushing's syndrome', an endocrine abnormality with associated suprarenal abnormality. His leg ulcers were only incidental, but hastened amyloid disease and renal and liver failure.

A forensic examination of his remains, which are in St George's Chapel, might well provide an unambiguous conclusion.

Edward VI

Born Westminster, 12 October 1537
Died Greenwich, 6 July 1553

A T T W O O ' C L O C K in the morning on Friday 12 October 1537, Jane Seymour at long last gave birth to a healthy male child. She had been in labour for no less than three days, and the length of her delivery was to cause the development of post-partum sepsis, which led to her death some 12 days later.

Following the birth, there was immense rejoicing. Te Deums were sung in St Paul's and in all the churches of the city, guns were fired from the Tower and many bonfires blazed. Wine and beer flowed in profusion – at long last England had a Prince of Wales who had indisputably been born in wedlock. To his father, Henry VIII, the birth was a vindication for the divorce of one wife and execution of another.

Edward was quite a sturdy little boy, who seems to have had no important childhood illnesses. He was christened in the chapel at Hampton Court with great pomp, with the Dukes of Suffolk and Norfolk and Archbishop Cranmer as his godfathers. His sister Mary was godmother. His other sister, Elizabeth, was intended to carry the heavy jewelled baptismal robe, but it proved to be too heavy and she was in fact carried in the procession by Queen Jane's brother.

Edward had a nurse to whom he became very attached, a certain Sybil Penn. It was only too natural that this should happen after the death of his mother. Visiting diplomats and officials noticed that when Edward was obliged to receive them, he clung to his nurse. In recognition of her services, Henry VIII gave her a single necklace of pearls, which is still in the collection of the Howe family. When Edward became King, he gave Sybil an apartment in Hampton Court next to that of Will Somers, the jester, who was such a friend to Henry VIII in his dotage.

The young prince was kept at court under the eye of his father, then in the summer moved to the country, where very elaborate precautions were taken to avoid his having any infection. In his own handwriting, Henry VIII gave orders regarding the care of his son: no person of the prince's privy council might go to London without permission and if anyone had to go, he would be forced into a period of quarantine before rejoining his duties; those who fell ill were to be removed immediately; everything was to be kept scrupulously clean with the galleries and rooms being scrubbed out twice a day; all he touched had to be washed and handled only by his personal servants; and all dogs were excluded. Under these sensible rules Edward prospered. His teeth appeared without difficulty; at one year old he was thinner, but getting taller and trying to walk; and he was soon a large, fair and healthy child, placid and fond of music.

Then, during the Christmas of 1541, Edward became ill. He developed what was described as a malarial type of fever and lost a lot of weight, causing great anxiety. It is quite possible that he had at this time a tuberculous infection, contracted in spite of all the precautions which his father had taken to avoid any such infection. The condition was to remain with him, in a latent form, for the rest of his short life. Spending much of his time at Greenwich, he improved slowly during 1542, and in the following year Henry was able to negotiate the Treaty of Greenwich, by which the young prince was to marry Mary, Queen of Scots. The proposed union faltered after Henry made impossible demands.

In 1544, a third Act of Succession was passed, giving Henry the right to dispose of the crown at will. However, it was made clear that should Edward fail to have issue and Henry fail to have any by his last marriage, then the crown would pass to Mary and then to Elizabeth. We find that it was this act that the then Duke of Northumberland was unsuccessfully trying to replace as the young King was dying some six years later.

Henry died in 1547 and Edward became King, with a council of 14 to help him govern during his minority. They were soon to appoint a lord protector in the form of his uncle Edward Seymour, Earl of Hertford. Edward was at Hertford Castle when he became King and it was from here that he made his progress to London.

At this time, he is described as a child with large grey eyes and the reddish-gold hair of the family. He was a very intelligent boy, but of a somewhat grave disposition and very serious minded. On 20 February he was crowned with great pomp and festivities – apparently what interested the young King most was an acrobat who performed on a rope stretched above St Paul's Churchyard.

From 1547 to 1550 Edward was under the care of his uncle, Edward Seymour, now Duke of Somerset. He became very fond of hunting and took regular exercise. Free from medical complaints, he was growing to be a very thin, fair youth, who took his position as king most seriously, particularly in the observation of all matters of religion. His sister Mary became estranged in her wish to continue with the Catholic religion of her mother, with Mass and priests in attendance. Elizabeth, on the other hand, indirectly created problems for a different reason. Thomas Seymour, the protector's brother, had married Catherine Parr, the widow of Henry VIII. They had one child, Mary, but following this Catherine developed puerperal sepsis and died. While she had been alive, she looked after Elizabeth, during which time her husband Thomas established a liaison with Elizabeth. This relationship was seen by many as being far too intimate. With the death of his wife, Thomas became increasingly ambitious and possibly eyed Elizabeth as a match. He also sought to share power with his brother. As a result, he came to be accused of treason, and was executed.

The position of Edward, Duke of Somerset, as lord protector was not to last for long. The Earl of Warwick amassed a small army and this enabled him to replace Somerset. This started a new period in the young King's life, where he took a much more active part in government. His relationship with his sister Mary continued to give him trouble, as she fought to continue with her Catholic faith. Elizabeth, on the other hand, presented no such difficulty, living at Hatfield or at Ashridge, and keeping away from court as much as possible, appearing there only once or twice a year.

The Earl of Warwick was created Duke of Northumberland in 1551. The future now depended on Edward marrying and producing a male heir to replace Mary and Elizabeth. At the age of 14, he appeared healthy enough, becoming very interested in sports, including tennis, which he played regularly and with reasonable skill. He was active at the tiltyard and at the butts, and the French ambassador complimented him on his swordplay. All seemed to be progressing satisfactorily.

Everything changed in April 1552. The King himself recorded: 'I fell sike of the measles and the smallpookes.' He no doubt had an acute attack of measles, not smallpox. He recovered enough to attend a service at Westminster Abbey, wearing his Garter robes. On 27 June he set off on a tour through the south and west, which was very exhausting; it was noticed that he looked very pale and thin. There is no doubt that the measles had activated a latent pulmonary tuberculosis. Measles is very apt to be followed by pulmonary complications, even in a fit person, and in one who has latent tuberculosis it is particularly dangerous. By the time he returned to Windsor, shortly after his fifteenth birthday, Edward was far from well, suffering a persistent cough, severe weight loss and exhaustion. Over the Christmas festivities, it became obvious to all that he was seriously ill.

In February Mary came to London and called upon her brother. Edward was confined to bed and it was three days before he felt well enough to see her. Mary sat with him and they chatted amicably enough, avoiding any subject of religion.

In March he improved slightly and opened the new session of Parliament with a curtailed service. He was by now, however, emaciated and his left shoulder was higher than his right. He was also emitting copious amounts of sputum, which was sometimes blood-tinged. It was decided that the healthy air of Greenwich would be better for him and he was accordingly removed there. A bulletin at the time reported: 'The physicians are all now agreed that he is suffering from a suppurative tumour on the lung. He is beginning to break out in ulcers; he is vexed with a harsh and continuous cough, his body is dry and burning, his belly is swollen, he had a slow fever upon him that never leaves him.'

The clinical picture is plainly one of generalised tuberculous infection. The ulcers were possibly pressure sores caused by his enforced long stay in bed. The swelling of the belly would have been caused by tuberculous peritonitis with associated ascites (fluid in the peritoneal cavity).

There now followed a dreadful period where Northumberland struggled to keep the young King alive for his own purposes. Knowing that Henry had bequeathed the crown to the Suffolk line, after his own children, he was aware of the possibility of Lady Jane Grey becoming Queen. He therefore hid the real state of the King's health, as he was anxious that neither Mary nor Elizabeth should visit Edward. Mary wrote several letters to Edward, but it is unlikely that they were delivered; Elizabeth on one occasion set out to see him, but before she could reach London she was given a message that Edward would not see her. Northumberland also arranged for his own son, Guildford, to marry Lady Jane Grey. This was in spite of the fact that she did not wish to marry him and had been on the point of marrying the young Earl of Hertford, whom she sincerely liked. It was essential for Northumberland that he should keep Edward alive long enough for his plans to materialise. He therefore sent away all the doctors who had been looking after Edward and installed a 'wise woman' to look after him. She said that if she were given sole control, she would be able to improve him. She gave Edward 'restringents' of an unknown type, which did effect a temporary improvement, all that Northumberland required. He needed to keep Edward alive just long enough for him to complete a Device of the Succession, disinheriting Mary and Elizabeth and giving the crown to Lady Jane Grey and her male successors.

By now, Edward had lost most of his hair, and even his nails, fingers and toes were becoming gangrenous. It is not known what the wise woman had given him, but his doctors were allowed once again to attend him. He had not really eaten for three weeks and could hardly speak, but obviously longed for the relief of death.

During 5 July, a terrible storm struck England with lightning, torrential rain and winds of great severity. Areas were flooded and many houses and trees blown down. The steeple of Weobley Church was sent crashing through the roof of the church. The storm continued throughout the next day as the King lay dying. On the afternoon of 6 July, he died in the arms of his great friend Henry Stanley. The great storm continued.

John Hayward in his *Life of Edward VI* writes:

> In April, in the sixth year of the reign of the King, he fell sick of the measles, whereof in a short time he well recovered; afterwards he

sickened of the smallpox which breaking kindly upon him, was
thought would prove a means to cleans his body from such
unhealthy humours as occasion long sickness and death; and
himself he also so perfectly recovered that in the summer next following he rode his progress with greater magnificence then ever
before. Soon afterwards the King did complain of a constant infirmity of the body, yet rather as an indisposition in health than any
set sickness. In January, about the beginning of the seventh year of
the symptoms of a tough, strong, strained cough. All the medicines and diet which could be prescribed, together with the help of
his young age and of the rising time of the year, were so far either
from curing or abating his grief that it daily increased by dangerous degrees, and it was not only a violence of the cough that did
infect him, but therewith a weakness and faintness of the spirit.
The King's sickness daily increased. His physicians discerning an
invincible malignity in his disease, his disease was violent and yet
they conceived some hope of a recovery in case he might be
removed to change of healthful air. A gentlewoman offered her
services assuredly to cure him in case he were committed wholly
to her hand. It was resolved that the physicians should be discharged and the cure committed to her alone. Within a very short
time the King did fall into desperate extremities. His vital parts
were mortally stuffed, which brought him to a difficulty of speech
and breath; his legs swelled; his pulse failed, his skin changed
colour and other symptoms appeared. The King, having long
wrestled with a lingering and tormenting sickness, at the last his
spirits yielded to the malice of the distemper. The Lords of the
Privy Council sent the news abroad, assigning the cause of his
death to be a putrefaction.

We can confidently say that Edward died of pulmonary tuberculosis aggravated by an attack of measles, followed by generalised
tuberculous infection and the misuse of stimulants of an unknown
type.

Lady Jane Grey

❧

Born 1537
Executed Tower of London, 1554

T HE EVENTS which led up to the death of Lady Jane Grey really began on Bosworth Field. As described in the chapter on Richard III, the King carved his way towards the position of Henry Tudor, until only one man, William Brandon, who had taken the standard of Cadwallader as standard-bearer, stood between him and Henry. Richard struck Brandon down and the standard fell, but at this moment the forces of Stanley overwhelmed Richard.

Henry Tudor was well aware of the service he had been done by the Brandon family and both he and his son furthered their cause. Thomas Brandon, the son of William, became a great friend of Henry VIII, for they both grew up together; so great was their friendship that Henry made Brandon Duke of Suffolk. For reasons of state, Henry's sister, Mary, was married to the aged King of France; it was a marriage to which she agreed on the condition that on his death she would be allowed to marry the man of her own choice. She did not have long to wait, as the King was dead in a few months. Mary then returned to England and married Thomas Brandon, who had obviously always been her own choice. They had a healthy daughter, Frances, who married Henry Grey, also a Duke of Suffolk. Together they had three daughters, all of very small stature, the youngest so small as to be almost a dwarf. The eldest daughter was Jane, who was of reasonable health, but only 5 feet tall. She was a very active and intelligent girl with an attractive disposition and personality, and was very popular with her friends. She was promised in marriage to the young Earl of Hertford, an arrangement she seems to have welcomed.

When it became clear that Edward VI's health was failing, his council, under the Duke of Northumberland, had reason to worry. Should Edward die, the crown would pass to his sister Mary, from whom Northumberland could expect little. He sought to maintain his position at all costs and the obvious course was to support the Suffolks, who, according to the will of Henry VIII, were to inherit if Mary and Elizabeth had no issue. Edward VI was very averse to his sister Mary becoming Queen, as he knew that she would restore the Catholic faith and thus all the work of his father would be lost. To prevent this Edward was very willing to support the Suffolk cause, readily agreeing to support Northumberland in his scheme to place the eldest of the Grey children, Lady Jane, on the throne. When it became obvious to Edward that he was indeed about to die, he gathered his council about him and tried to make them all sign a document to this effect. If Edward had lived some time longer he would have been able to pass through Parliament another Act of Succession which would have given Jane full parliamentary backing. Unfortunately for Jane he did not, in spite of Northumberland's desperate efforts to keep him alive.

Edward VI died on 6 July 1553, but it was not until 9 July that Northumberland showed his hand. This lack of resolve seems rather strange, as he was a very fine soldier and an able administrator. For Northumberland's cause to be effective, it was essential that he should have control of both Mary and Elizabeth, and in both cases he failed. He sent a message to Mary calling on her to visit her dying brother. She set out, but was warned that this was a ruse to get her under his control and she returned to the safety of Kenninghall in Norfolk. Northumberland sent off 300 horses, under the command of his son Robert, to capture Mary, but this they failed to do, which left Mary with the opportunity to form a supporting party before further action was taken.

While Edward was ill, but still alive, Northumberland had married his eldest son, Guildford, to Lady Jane Grey. In this matter he encountered considerable opposition from Jane herself, who planned to marry Hertford and had no liking for the conceited Guildford. She was only 15 years old, but had considerable determination and both Northumberland and her family took great pains to persuade her to obey their wishes. She was married at the end of

May. Jane insisted on going back to her parents' home at Sheen immediately after her wedding, but was forced by the families to return to her new husband at Durham House, where the marriage was consummated. She stayed only a few days and then became so ill that it was agreed she should go to Chelsea to recuperate.

On 9 July she was summoned to Syon House where she met with the council, members of her own and her husband's family, and with Northumberland. He told her that her cousin Edward had nominated her as his successor. All showed suitable deference to her position. The following day, Jane was taken by water to the Tower, accompanied by Guildford, dressed all in white. She was installed in the royal apartments at the Tower and was visited by the Lord Treasurer, the Marquis of Winchester. He brought some of the royal jewels for her to inspect and also a crown which he asked her to wear. Jane recoiled in horror. Winchester told her that she could wear it as a right and that they would make another for her husband to wear. This was the last straw: she was adamant that never would she make her husband King; a duke but never King. A row immediately blew up, with Guildford saying that he would leave his ungrateful wife and return to Syon. Jane simply ordered the Lords Arundel and Pembroke to prevent him from leaving.

Heralds were now sent round the city to proclaim Jane Queen. This got little support from the populace. Mary, meanwhile, sent a letter from Kenninghall to the council demanding that they proclaim her right to the throne. Every day, further forces flocked to her cause. Northumberland gathered his forces to meet her. He decided to put Suffolk in charge of this army, but Jane begged him not to send her father away. Northumberland realised that he himself would have to command the forces and on 14 July he rode out of London.

News came in that Mary's forces were multiplying, while Northumberland's were deserting. Ships, sent to Yarmouth to make sure that Mary could not escape, transferred their allegiance to her. When this became known, the desertions became more and more frequent: Arundel, Pembroke and many others made their excuses and left. Old Winchester tried to desert and was brought back. Jane stood more and more alone.

On 19 July 1553 Mary was proclaimed Queen. The Duke of Suffolk and his party left the Tower to return to Sheen and Jane was left alone. She pleaded that she had never courted the crown and that her position was created by others. This was accepted and no further action was taken against her, although she was detained in the Tower.

Mary's relationship with her sister Elizabeth worsened as religious matters came to a head. She herself was pressed to marry and it was hoped that she would choose an Englishman. But Mary was offered the hand of Philip of Spain, which she eagerly accepted. To many this was a match to be resisted at all costs and risings took place in Devonshire, Wales and Kent. All came to very little, except the Kent rising, led by Thomas Wyatt. Supported by the navy, he advanced on London. The Londoners supported Mary and fighting ensued. By 7 February, the Queen's forces were victorious.

This rebellion sealed the fate of Lady Jane. Further possible risings could have used her and her husband as rallying points for those opposed to Mary and her Catholic husband. It was with great reluctance that Mary was persuaded that Jane should die, and many of those who had supported Jane now called for her death: Arundel, Winchester, Pembroke and others. Mary decided she would at least try to save the soul of her cousin and sent Dr Feckenham, the Abbot of Westminster, to convert her.

Jane was living in the Tower in pleasant enough quarters, with three women to serve her. She was under the care of a gentleman gaoler and his wife, who treated her with respectful consideration. Dr Feckenham arrived and had several interesting debates with her, but the good doctor had no success in converting her from her faith. There is no doubt that the two developed a great respect for one another. Jane prepared to die by writing letters and giving away possessions. Mary had decreed that Jane and her husband be allowed to meet for a farewell; Jane refused this offer.

The execution took place on 12 February. Her husband, Guildford, was to be executed on Tower Hill, but the place of her own execution was a small scaffold on Tower Green. On the morning of 12 February, Jane sat at her window in the Tower and watched her husband pass on his way to his execution, then waited for the cart containing his body to return to the small chapel of St Peter Vincula. She seems to have been a very self-possessed young girl for one of only 16.

It was now the turn of Jane to face death. She emerged from her residence in the Tower on the arm of the Lieutenant of the Tower, Sir John Brydges, who had great sympathy for the brave young girl. She was allowed two attendant ladies and chose Nurse Ellen and Mrs Tilney to go with her. They were deeply upset, but Jane herself mounted the scaffold with great composure, her prayer book in her hand. Dr Feckenham was in attendance, as he had promised he would be. She made a short speech in which she said that she looked to be saved 'by none other mean, but only by the mercy of God in the merits of the blood of his only son Jesus Christ'. She ended, 'While I am alive, I pray you to assist me with your prayers.' She knelt and repeated the 51st Psalm in English; at her side Feckenham followed in Latin. She handed her gloves and handkerchief to Mrs Tilney and her prayer book to the brother of John Brydges. She had started to undo her dress when the executioner stepped forward to assist her, but 'she desired him to leave her alone.' Her two attendants helped her to take off her overgarments. They gave her 'a fair handkerchief to knit about her eyes'. The executioner knelt and asked for forgiveness, which was given. The handkerchief was bound round her eyes. At this point her nerve seemed to leave her for a moment and she cried, 'What shall I do? Where is it?' Her attendants guided her forward and 'she laid down upon the block and stretched forth her body and said, "Lord, into thy hands I commend my spirit."' The axe swung and she was dead. Her very small body was taken away and placed under stones in the small chapel of St Peter Vincula, close to the bodies of two former queens, Anne Boleyn and Catherine Howard.

Mary I

∼

Born Westminster, 11 February 1516
Died St James's Palace, 17 November 1558

Some say she died of a tinpany, others of grief conceived. Others that her liver being over-cooled by a mola and not being taken in time, cast her into a dropsy, which the physicians call asiatica. She [having] not observed a fit diet fell into a fever, which increasing little by little at last put an end to her life, which fever at that time raged in most of England and swept away a great number of people. (From *The Life of Mary*, published in 1682)

T HE ABOVE is a reference to what was known as the 'sweating sickness', a somewhat unusual disease resembling influenza. By this time it had occurred in at least three epidemics.

Mary was the child of the fourth pregnancy of Catherine of Aragon. It is of some interest to consider the obstetric history of Catherine of Aragon, since it is somewhat unusual. Her first pregnancy in 1510 resulted in a daughter, who was unfortunately stillborn. At this time, it was more usual for women to have a normal birth in their early pregnancies, as there was less time for them to develop the hypochromic anaemia from which they all tended to suffer. Her second pregnancy, a year later, produced a live son, but there does not appear to have been great rejoicing at this birth, so it must have been appreciated that the child was unlikely to live. He was christened Henry and survived for only seven weeks. A third pregnancy, in 1513, resulted in another stillborn daughter, the next to a son who lived for a few days. By this time, both Catherine and Henry were starting to despair of ever having a live child. So in 1516, when Catherine gave birth to a daughter who appeared to be of reasonable health, this was most welcome and gave rise to the hope that the next pregnancy might produce a live male. Catherine did not feed her baby on the breast, instead passing her to a wet nurse. This would increase the possibility of Catherine becoming pregnant again, but she was now likely to have been suffering from severe anaemia and was also approaching the menopause. She did, however, become pregnant for the last time in 1518, which resulted in another stillborn daughter. It seemed that she was indeed incapable of producing an heir for Henry, a circumstance made all the more unfortunate in 1519, when Henry had a healthy son by Elizabeth Blount.

We know that at the age of 11 Mary was in good health, for in May 1527 she played a major part in entertaining foreign ambassadors at Greenwich. There she danced to perfection and is said to have dazzled the company with her performance. Her father was justly proud and took off her cap and hairnet to display her 'perfusion of silver tresses as beautiful as ever seen on human head'; as a child her hair was fair, but by the age of 18 it had darkened. She seems also to have had a good complexion and a small, well-proportioned physique.

As Mary grew up, her environment became increasingly difficult. Her mother was displaced by Anne Boleyn; the worst period for Mary and her mother was the time just before the birth of Elizabeth in 1533. Mary's health altered, as she was subject to considerable nervous strain: her periods became very irregular and she also suffered from recurrent headache and possible sleeplessness. Her health did not improve and her face showed the strain. She was very fond of music and of dancing, but had little or no opportunity to indulge. She was also drawn to children, even being attracted to the infant Elizabeth, the child of the hated Anne.

In his last years, her father realised that he was to have no further children and centred all his attention on Edward. At first the young Edward had a reasonable relationship with his elder sister Mary. When he became King, however, Edward started to worry about Mary's continued practice of the Catholic faith and he attempted, unsuccessfully, to persuade her to renounce it. This increased her stress and she became increasingly prone to illness. Unlike her sister Elizabeth, who frequently used the excuse of illness, Mary really was unwell. Her major trial was to come with the death of her brother. She set out to visit her dying brother, but was warned that this would be dangerous. Gathering her forces together, she defeated the Duke of Northumberland's scheme to place Jane Grey on the throne. This period was the one in which she showed the best side of her character, displaying courage and determination. Her health seems to have been somewhat better at this time.

The idea that she should marry, have a husband and possibly children of her own, had great attraction for her. She made efforts to marry a person from her mother's home, Spain, which seemed to many in England to be a grave mistake, and in fact caused the Wyatt Rebellion. When she accepted the proposal of Philip of Spain, she was overjoyed and her marriage on 25 July 1554, at Winchester, was the highlight of her life. In spite of her age – she was 38 – she felt that she could have a child as she still menstruated, although irregularly. Also, her husband was young, being ten years her junior. She had genuine affection for him and no doubt came to love him; he, on the other hand, seems merely to have tolerated her. At the time of her marriage, she was worn, flat-chested, with an indifferent complexion and a voice which had become very harsh, almost masculine. Her hair was somewhat thin and she was very small in stature, although so too was Philip.

By November, Mary thought that she was pregnant. Her abdomen was increasing in size and she noticed changes in her breasts. At this time the country had become reunited with Rome and great efforts were made to marry her sister Elizabeth to a Catholic prince, but to no avail. So all depended on the Queen being brought to bed with a healthy child.

In April 1555 Mary was moved to Hampton Court in preparation for her lying-in. The cradle was in place in the same rooms in which Edward Tudor had been born, and there were numerous midwives and nurses in attendance. In order to encourage the Queen, triplets, in fine health, were brought for her to see. They had just been born to a woman of considerable age and small stature, like the Queen.

On 30 April a rumour spread to London that Mary had been delivered of a fine boy and there was universal rejoicing. Then came news that this was untrue and the waiting began again. The days passed; it was stated that miscalculations had been made and the birth would now be in late May. Mary decreased in size and the doctors put this down to the head of foetus having moved down into the pelvis. There was no doubt, though, that her abdomen was becoming smaller, and as the weeks passed, it became increasingly clear that the Queen was not 'with child'. However, her amenorrhoea persisted.

To Mary's bitter disappointment, Philip now decided to return home to Spain, albeit with a promise that he would return. On 26 August the court moved down to Greenwich to see him off and thus Mary lost her husband and the possibility of becoming pregnant again.

At the end of March 1557, Philip returned. Meanwhile Mary had been suffering from very poor health, with various periods of abdominal enlargement and gastro-intestinal upsets. By this time, Philip seems to have been of the opinion that Elizabeth should be recognised as Mary's successor and that the best policy would be to marry her to a suitable husband. To Mary, though, this would mean the ultimate triumph of the hated Anne Boleyn. As for Philip, he had returned for only one reason – to try to involve England in the Franco-Spanish war. When it became obvious by July that England was not going to agree to his scheme, he decided once again to leave. On this occasion Mary went down to Dover to see him off, sensing perhaps that this was to be their last meeting. Then, once again, Mary thought that she was pregnant. On this occasion she decided to wait to make sure that she was right; after a few months she found that, as before, all the signs were false.

The year 1558 brought another disaster in the loss of Calais, the last English stronghold in France. The Queen was also becoming increasingly ill with loss of weight and appetite. There is no doubt that she had some abdominal abnormality, most probably an ovarian cystic tumour, which would have accounted for her abdominal enlargement; cancer of the ovary or possibly of the uterus seems the most likely cause. In November Philip sent a representative to her; on his arrival, it was obvious that nothing could be done. The Queen was now lapsing into periods of near unconsciousness with short lucid intervals. In one of these periods her council did persuade her to accept Elizabeth being named as her successor, although with some difficulty. She agreed only on the understanding that Elizabeth was to maintain her sister's religion and pay all of her debts.

In one of her lucid moments, Mary comforted her attendants by saying that, while unconscious, she had had good dreams of many little children playing. These lucid intervals, followed by periods of unconsciousness, continued for a considerable time, a condition which was fairly painless. Gradually Mary wasted away, with less and less knowledge of her surroundings. The end came early in the morning of 17 November.

Mary was buried in a fine tomb in Westminster Abbey. Elizabeth paid for this and also settled most of her sister's debts. Mary's heart was removed and placed in a casket, into which Elizabeth's heart was also finally placed. In death the two sisters lie together, with one tomb above the other. Unfortunately the heavy tomb of Elizabeth is now pressing down on that of Mary, and it may well require some restoration in the near future.

Elizabeth I

❧

Born Greenwich, 7 September 1533
Died Richmond, 24 March 1603

She feeling some infirmities of old age and sickness retired herself at the end of January to Richmond. At the beginning of her sickness the almonds of her jaws began to swell and her appetite, little by little, failed her. In March, a kind of denumbness seized upon her with a deep melanchology, so that she would sit silently, refrain her meat, and not admit any confidence but with the Archbishop of Canterbury, with whom she prayed feverently till such time as her speech failed her, which failed before she died. (From Baker's *Chronicle*)

HENRY VIII courted Elizabeth's mother, Anne Boleyn, for the unbelievable period of some six years before she consented to have sexual relationships with him. This finally happened in October 1532, when Anne was created Marchioness of Pembroke and given an income of £1,000 a year. The following January, Henry and Anne were secretly married by the King's chaplain in Whitehall. There is no doubt that Henry knew Anne to be pregnant and was anxious that the child should be born in wedlock. In February 1533, Anne is said to have come from her room and announced that for some three days she had felt a great desire to eat apples. The King told her that this was a sign that she was with child, but Anne denied that this could be so, although she must have known that she was indeed pregnant.

On 1 June 1533 Anne was crowned queen. She went in procession to Westminster 'under a canopy of cloth of gold, wearing a kirtle of

crimson velvet under a robe of purple velvet furred with ermine'.
The crown was carried by Charles Brandon, Earl of Suffolk, and her
two sceptres by two other earls. In the abbey, she was anointed by
the Archbishops of Canterbury and York. Her procession through
the city was somewhat marred by the fact that few shouted her
praise and many refused to doff their caps. Still, so long as she was
with child and that child was a male, nothing else mattered.

Henry had been convinced by the court physicians and
astrologers that the child was to be a male. He decided to celebrate
the birth with a pageant and a tournament. In August the court was
moved from Windsor to Greenwich so that the child might be born
where Henry had himself been born. On Sunday 7 September Anne
gave birth, with slight difficulty, to a 'fair daughter'. Henry was bitterly disappointed – another useless girl. Far from securing the succession he had, in fact, made it a little more insecure by introducing
an element of doubt into the royal lineage. Nevertheless, a Te Deum
was sung in St Paul's Cathedral for Anne's safe delivery and the
child was christened Elizabeth, after her grandmother, in the Friars
Church at Greenwich.

So Elizabeth came into the world, a somewhat unwanted girl.
Anne's further history is well known. She became pregnant with a
male child, only to abort after Henry suffered a severe injury in the
joust. She then fell further from grace, ultimately to be executed.
Elizabeth was barely three years old and could not have fully appreciated what was happening to her mother. Indeed, she had spent
very little time with Anne and it is very likely that in later life she
had no memory of her. When she was Queen she certainly did not
make any effort to have Anne removed from the small chapel in the
Tower and reburied, unlike James I, who reburied his mother,
Mary, Queen of Scots, in a magnificent tomb in Westminster
Abbey.

As we saw earlier, it has sometimes been suggested that Elizabeth
was born of a syphilitic father. I feel that this is most unlikely as
Elizabeth never in her lifetime showed any trace of such a disease
and at a slightly later date Henry sired a healthy boy with Elizabeth
Blount.

Elizabeth grew up into an active and intelligent child. She must
have become aware of her mother's execution and disgrace as she
was referred to as a 'royal bastard'. From the time that she was three,

the council discussed the possibility of her marriage to a foreign prince. She was indeed an attractive proposition for a political marriage and France, Bohemia and Savoy all considered the possibility. When Elizabeth was nine, Henry VIII attempted to woo Scotland by marrying his son Edward to Mary, Queen of Scots, and Elizabeth to Lord Arran. Henry expected too much, however, and the matches fell through. Two years later it was proposed that Mary should marry the Emperor Charles V and Elizabeth should marry his son, Philip of Spain. This was not accepted because Mary and Elizabeth were declared to be 'illegitimate' and thus not considered safe marriages.

Thomas Seymour, the brother of Edward Seymour, Duke of Somerset, was to play an important part in the life and medical history of Elizabeth. When his brother became Lord Protector to Edward VI, Thomas became ambitious on his own behalf. He had been a possible husband for Catherine Parr before she caught the eye of Henry VIII and became queen. Some four months after the death of the King, Thomas married his former love, Catherine. Before doing so, he sent a love letter to Elizabeth, asking for her hand in marriage; he was politely refused. And yet, when Thomas and Catherine set up house at Chelsea, Elizabeth went to live with them, a somewhat unusual arrangement. She had by this time developed into a very attractive young woman: she was of reasonable height (many of the women of this time were very small), with a good complexion and a fine head of golden-red hair; she also had very attractive slim hands.

Thomas now proceeded to flirt with Elizabeth under the eyes of his wife. Perhaps his wife thought that she and her husband would benefit from a close relationship with one who might become Queen. Certainly, the relationship appears to have grown intimate, as Thomas was apt to go into Elizabeth's bedroom while she was in bed; he would try to kiss her and slap her buttocks and even climb into bed with her. On one occasion, Thomas chased her in the garden, and when he caught her, Catherine helped to hold Elizabeth down while he cut her dress so that he could see her body and underclothes. Matters came to a head when Catherine found Thomas and Elizabeth in a passionate embrace and realised that the matter had gone far enough. Elizabeth was sent away to Hatfield.

How far this experience affected Elizabeth in later life we can only surmise. Thomas was to stand trial for treason, while Elizabeth was accused of being pregnant by him. She obviously had considerable affection for him and his subsequent execution must have been a great blow. On his death, she is reported as saying: 'This day died a man with much wit and very little judgement.' Did his rough behaviour and fierce advances cause her to repulse others as she grew up? The remote possibility of her having been pregnant by him and having to hide the fact in later life is an interesting but unlikely speculation. At the age of 18 Elizabeth was even more attractive. She was considered for marriage with both the King of Navarre and the King of Denmark's son, but she did not wish this and made her thoughts plain. She also refused the Earl of Pembroke. It is said too that the Duke of Northumberland considered divorce so that he might marry her and rule on the death of Edward.

For Elizabeth, all went well until the Wyatt Rebellion, which aimed to usurp Mary and replace her with Elizabeth and Edward Courtenay, who was considered to be a suitable husband. Courtenay was of the Yorkist line and had spent much of his life in the Tower of London after his father was executed by Henry VIII. He and Elizabeth had been very friendly and had recently renewed their relationship. Mary's suspicion of her sister was confirmed by the rebellion and she had her arrested and then sent to the Tower. Released after two months of anxious waiting, Elizabeth was sent under house arrest to Woodstock. Here she agreed to attend Mass as requested, but the strain of the past months began to show and she became ill, prone to outbursts of anger and weeping. Her face became swollen which suggests a mild endocrine abnormality which slowly resolved itself. Her outbursts persisted.

After Mary married Philip of Spain, Elizabeth was brought to court in 1555. Philip seems to have been attracted to Elizabeth and she owed much of her new-found liberty to his intervention. He did, though, stress the need for her to marry a good Catholic.

Meanwhile, Mary conducted her policy of religious reformation, burning both heretics and Protestants. Elizabeth bided her time with protestations of loyalty, while Philip and Mary became more and more unpopular. Then on 17 November 1558, Mary died and Elizabeth became Queen.

Before her coronation, which was performed by the Bishop of Carlisle as the archbishops refused to take part, Elizabeth received a letter from Philip of Spain asking for her hand in marriage. He wrote several 'love letters' to her, which gave her great pleasure and appealed to her vanity, but she refused to marry. Her excuse was a very neat argument: if Philip could marry the sister of his former wife, then it was quite correct that Henry VIII married Catherine of Aragon, a fact which made his second marriage and Elizabeth, his second daughter, illegitimate.

Parliament was called shortly after Elizabeth's coronation. It requested that the Queen should marry to secure the throne. Elizabeth once again declared that she had no intention of marrying, 'and in the end this shall for me be sufficient, that a marble stone shall declare that a Queen, having reigned such a time, lived and died a virgin'. It is most interesting that she was very keen to be considered a virgin – it almost seems to be overstressed. Had she been put off all sex by her affair with Thomas?

Elizabeth encountered severe opposition to her re-establishment of a Protestant state. She was forced to dismiss several bishops and appoint her own. She indulged herself with frequent outbursts of petulant anger, probably the result of frustration and a sense of impotence. These outbursts were to continue throughout her reign and her advisors came to expect such behaviour if she disagreed with them: they might be slapped on the face or dismissed for a while. Unlike that of her father, though, her anger was limited and short-lived.

In the first two years of her reign, difficulties arose with her infatuation with her Master of Horse, Robert Dudley. He was the younger son of John Dudley, Earl of Warwick and Duke of Northumberland. After the defeat of the plot to put Lady Jane Grey on the throne, the Dudley children were put in the Tower with their father. He was executed and the children were then allowed to go free. Robert was brought up at court and knew Elizabeth from the time that they were both children. At the age of 17 he married Amy Robsart, the daughter of a Norfolk gentleman of no special importance. At the age of 26 he was made Master of Horse, as soon as Elizabeth came to the throne. He played an active part in the court and Elizabeth was obviously very attracted to him, praising him on all possible occasions, having his rooms moved next to her own and making him a knight of the Garter. Rumours spread of a love affair. It was even rumoured that she was pregnant by him and that he intended to poison his own wife and marry Elizabeth. Elizabeth's advisors reminded her that her position was likely to be compromised. At this point, Amy Robsart was found dead, of a broken neck, at the foot of the stairs in her house at Cumnor. Her attendants had been absent on the day in question. It was now impossible for Elizabeth to marry Dudley, as her position would have been untenable. She also discounted her plan to make Dudley the Earl of Leicester.

Elizabeth had another danger to face from Mary, Queen of Scots. Her cousin had married the King of France, Francis II, but at the age of 16 he developed otitis media and from this a mastoid infection, complicated by a deadly extradural abscess. He died and Mary returned to Scotland. If Elizabeth had now married (thus virtually guaranteeing a Protestant heir), it is possible that English Catholics would have risen and, with Scottish help, made Mary Queen.

In 1559, Elizabeth became ill. It is not quite clear what her complaint was, but she developed a recurrent fever. It was a tertian fever, possibly malaria. There was no associated coughing, such as would have been present with a tuberculous infection, a disease which was the scourge of the Tudors. She took some time to recover and the danger to her life stressed how important it was for her to have children.

The two next in line to the throne had an interesting but somewhat sad story. They were the two sisters of Lady Jane Grey. The elder, Catherine Grey, had wanted to marry Edward Seymour, Somerset's son who was Earl of Hertford. Elizabeth was opposed to this marriage, as together they would have had a very strong claim to the throne. However, they were married secretly and Catherine became pregnant. Elizabeth was furious, even more so when a strong boy was born. The couple were put in the Tower of London, where a lax gaoler allowed them to meet; once again Catherine became pregnant with a boy. This was too much for Elizabeth, who left Seymour in the Tower and released Catherine. They were never to meet again as Catherine died in 1568. Her sister, Mary, was a very small person, so small as to be almost a dwarf. She fell in love with the Queen's porter, a certain Thomas Keys, who was very strong and tall. Again, Elizabeth was upset and imprisoned Keys in the Fleet Prison, while Mary was kept under house arrest. The little Mary always signed herself Mary Keys. Keys died in prison in 1571; Mary lived another seven years.

By 1562 Elizabeth was negotiating to meet her cousin Mary, Queen of Scots. However, civil war broke out in France and England had to defend Le Havre. As a result, the meeting with Mary was postponed.

On 10 October 1562 Elizabeth was at Hampton Court when she complained of feeling unwell. It was thought by her doctors that she had caught a chill after having taken a bath. The following day she had a very high temperature, which persisted. She did not appear to have the sweating sickness (Sudor Anglicus) which the doctors feared. This disease tended to appear in epidemic form, the last severe outbreak being at the time Mary I had died. High fever and a frequently fatal outcome made the disease one of the most feared. After two days of continued high fever, Elizabeth developed the rash of smallpox. It was generalised over her body, but her face was affected only in a limited way. Her condition rapidly worsened and she became critically ill. She was fortunate in being cared for by Lady Mary Sidney, who devoted herself to the Queen in spite of the strong possibility of herself becoming infected. By 16 October, the physicians told the council that they thought the Queen's life to be in grave danger.

Lord Cecil and the council had to make an immediate decision as to how they should proceed in the event of Elizabeth's death. They chose to support Henry Hastings, now Earl of Huntingdon, as king. He was married to the sister of Robert Dudley, who formed a force of soldiers to support his brother-in-law. Mary, Queen of Scots and Katherine Grey were to be put aside.

The Queen's life now hung in the balance. However, in all cases of smallpox there is the possibility of sudden improvement and this is what occurred. Elizabeth made a very rapid recovery, so much so that within ten days she was able to leave her bed. She took some time to recover completely and her body was pockmarked, but not her face, a matter which had worried her lest she should have facial disfigurement; the elaborate make-up which she wore in later years was not to hide pockmarks. Poor Lady Mary Sidney also developed the disease and was severely disfigured.

Le Havre was now evacuated and the soldiers returned to the south of England. Unfortunately they brought back the plague with them, and London had a severe epidemic. It is said that 17,000 people died: one-sixth of the total population. Elizabeth escaped infection, but the Spanish ambassador was one of the victims.

Throughout Elizabeth's life, there were rumours and counter-rumours on the subject of her marriage. Although she appeared to be pleased to discuss any possible arrangement, she always contra-dicted any ultimate agreement. Perhaps the strangest of all these possible marriages relates to the Duke of Anjou. He was brother to Henry, the King of France, who had suggested the match. Elizabeth toyed with the idea for no less than seven years. In 1579 she agreed that he should visit England and he came and spent 13 days with her. She had heard that he was not a very attractive man but found this to be quite untrue; perhaps her feelings were accentuated by the fact that she was at this time 46, and he was a youth of 24. They got on very well together and it even appeared as if Elizabeth might be in love. This caused widespread alarm, as Anjou was a devout Catholic. A book criticising her actions was published which caused her such anger that the writer had his hand cut off. In 1581 Anjou again visited Elizabeth, once in secret and once on an official visit. On 22 November, in Whitehall, in the presence of the French ambassador and many others, Elizabeth took off one of the rings on her fingers and put it on the finger of Anjou saying that they were to be married.

France was delighted. The French King celebrated the engage-ment with a great ball held in the Louvre. However, there is no doubt that Elizabeth changed her mind after a few days, as she started to set impossible demands for the marriage. The engage-ment was broken. Why she had taken the matter so far before deciding once again against it is not clear.

The reasons why Elizabeth behaved in so peculiar a manner throughout her life have long been debated. Did she have some physical impediment to sexual intercourse, of which she was aware, but kept secret? Was she still a disappointed woman who had not been able to marry her true love, Robert Dudley? Had she had a child by one of her lovers? Was her action purely political? If she should fail to produce a child, then her crown would pass to the child of Mary, Queen of Scots, so it is perhaps surprising that she took no steps to marry.

Perhaps the reason for Elizabeth's strange behaviour is explained by events in June 1587, when the Spanish Armada was being prepared for the invasion of England the next year. A ship sailing to France was intercepted off San Sebastian. Among those on board was a young Englishman, aged about 25, who said that he had been on a pilgrimage to the Shrine of Our Lady of Monserrat, as a good Catholic, and was now returning to France. He was imprisoned, but asked to see Sir Francis Englefield, who had been Master of the Wards in the reign of Mary I and the only member of her government to choose exile on her death. The young man told him a strange tale.

He said that his real name was Arthur Dudley. As a child he had been brought up outside London with the family of Robert Southern, a servant of Katherine Ashley, the former governess of Queen Elizabeth. When he was five, he was taken to London and placed under the care of Katherine Ashley's husband, John. He was given a gentleman's education in French, Italian dancing, fencing and other matters. He spent his time in London and at Enfield with the Ashleys. At the age of 15 he wished to travel, but was told that this was not possible. Accordingly, he ran away and had reached Milford Haven when he was arrested and shown an order from the Privy Council saying that on no account was he to be allowed to leave the country. Enlisting in 1580, he volunteered to serve in the Netherlands and found himself taken to Ostend by a servant of Robert Dudley.

In 1582, he was told to return home to England, since his father was dying and wished to see him on an urgent matter. Southern then told him that he was not his real father, and that one day he had been summoned to Hampton Court on the orders of Katherine Ashley, where a new-born baby was handed to him by Lady Harrington. She revealed that the child was from one of the ladies of the court and Southern was asked to bring him up as his own son. Southern told Arthur that he was that baby and that his education had been paid for by Ashley. He also said that he knew the identity of the real father, but was unable to disclose this on his peril. However, as Southern approached death he told Arthur that he was the son of Robert Dudley, the Earl of Leicester and that the Queen was his mother. From the moment that he received this information, Arthur had been frightened lest he be murdered, either by followers of Leicester or on orders from the Queen.

Englefield was in doubt as to the truth of this story, so he devised several questions to test Arthur's knowledge of events in England and at the Ashley home. To all of these Arthur replied with no difficulty. There still remained the possibility that he might be a spy and that the story had been devised to prevent either James of Scotland or Philip of Spain from claiming the throne, so Englefield therefore told Philip of his findings. He felt that the best course to take would be to incarcerate Arthur in a monastery for the time being until his story could then be further investigated. There are, however, no further references to Arthur in the Spanish state papers. Was he the child of Elizabeth and was he the cause for her continued strange behaviour? We will never know.

As Elizabeth grew into an old woman, she did so with considerable grace, in that she still continued to ride, hunt and take exercise. Her wit and mental energy persisted, although her attacks of temper became more frequent and were often brought on by discussion of marriage. She often asked her ladies if they had any intention of marriage and she liked to hear the answer that the idea was repugnant to them. When the daughter of Robert Arundel, newly arrived at court, was asked the usual question, she did not know the correct answer and confessed that she would like to marry, but had not yet obtained her parents' consent. Elizabeth replied that the matter could be left to her and that she would gain the consent. This she did, and Arundel gave his consent in writing. Elizabeth sent for the young lady, and revealed that she had a consent in writing. 'Then I shall be happy,' said the girl. 'So thou shalt,' replied Elizabeth, 'but not to be a fool and marry. I have his consent given to me and I vow thou shalt never get it into thy possession. So go to thy business. I see thou girl a bold one to own thy foolishness readily.' Surely this is the behaviour of one who has a distorted and very morbid approach to marriage and all that follows.

The Essex Plot of 1601, which resulted in the execution of Essex, naturally upset Elizabeth who was becoming an old woman who had lost her latest amour.

She still continued, in spite of her age, with her 'progresses' throughout the country, although she remained closer to London. In 1602 she spent Christmas and New Year at Whitechapel. In January she caught a severe cold and a boil developed on her face. On 21 January she travelled to Richmond. It was a very cold and wet day, and she became ill again. It appears that she was having difficulty in swallowing, possibly associated with severe dental sepsis and decay. On 28 February she became ill once more, only to improve after a few days. On 20 March, as she was going into chapel, she collapsed and was taken into her privy chamber. She refused to be put into bed, but sat on the floor and cushions were brought for her comfort. She still had difficulty in taking any nourishment and the glands of her neck enlarged. It was felt that she would be better in bed and they managed, partly by persuasion and partly by force, to get her into bed. After a small improvement on 23 March, she lost the power of speech. Her final condition would have been one of bronchopneumonia secondary upon dental and oral sepsis with associated suppurative parotitis (inflammation of the parotid glands). This condition is rapidly followed by pneumonia in debilitated and aged persons.

In the early hours of 24 March 1603, the old Queen died. In spite of her instructions that her body was not to be embalmed, it was decided that this should be done. Was she still trying to hide some physical condition? Her embalmed body was taken to Westminster Abbey on 23 April, where her heart was enclosed in a casket with that of her sister Mary.

James I

~

Born 19 June 1566
Died Theobalds, 27 March 1625

The King being sick of a certain ague, and that in the spring was of itself never found deadly, the Duke of Buckingham took his opportunity, upon the Monday before the king died, and offered him a white powder to take, which he a long time refused, but overcome with his flattering importunity at length took it in some wine, and immediately became worse and worse, falling into many swoonings and pains and violent fluxes of the body. In like manner also, my Lady Buckingham upon the Friday after, applied a plaster to the kings heart and breast whereupon he grew faint and short-breathed and in great agony. The Sunday after his majesty died, and Buckingham desired the physicians who attended his Majesty to sign with their own hands, a writ of testimony that the powder that he gave him was a good safe medicine, which they refused. In the meanwhile, the Kings body and head swelled above measure, the hair with the skin of the head stuck to the pillow, and the nails became loose upon the fingers and toes. (From the *Harleian Misc.*, 1714)

THIS IS an obvious effort to discredit the Duke of Buckingham and accuses him of trying to poison James. However, the description is very similar to that given after the death of Edward VI, who, like James, probably died of pulmonary tuberculosis.

James had a tempestuous entry onto the stage of history. His mother, Mary, Queen of Scots, had been married to Francis II of France, who died in December 1560. Mary returned to Scotland, where she was to rule until 1567. She had considered a second marriage, and Elizabeth I even 'offered' her favourite Dudley (who later became Earl of Leicester) as a suitor, but he was rejected.

In February 1565, Henry Stuart Darnley, son of the Earl of Lennox, arrived in Scotland on a passport given to him by Elizabeth for three months. Darnley was of royal descent, as his father had married the daughter of Margaret Tudor, sister of Henry VIII. Mary herself was the granddaughter of Margaret. The union of Mary, Queen of Scots and Darnley would thus unite two claims to the throne, giving any offspring a very strong claim indeed. It seems puzzling that Elizabeth allowed Darnley to go to Scotland. She must have thought that a marriage was unlikely. Darnley contracted measles soon after his arrival and Mary helped in his nursing, becoming very attracted to the 'lustiest and best-proportioned lang man she had seen'. He was tall and beardless, so very different from the somewhat uncouth Scots. She created him Earl of Ross, which amounted to a betrothal.

Following the marriage in 1565, they planned to rule as Henry and Mary, King and Queen of the Scots. However, many Scottish nobles were affronted and a rebellion, led by Murray, broke out. Mary quickly defeated Murray, but she was soon to recognise that Darnley was a playboy and utterly unfit to be a king and consort. In the autumn of 1565, Mary became pregnant, which led to the unfounded suspicion that her favourite, Rizzio, an Italian musician, was the father. Those who had rebelled with Murray were awaiting trial and they agreed to support Darnley in his demand for the Crown Matrimonial (a parliamentary assurance of power during Mary's lifetime and after, consistently refused by her) if he would prevent any action against them. This conspiracy, which failed, was therefore to eliminate Mary. Rizzio was murdered and it is even said that a pistol was held at Mary's belly; James might have died within his mother. She survived the incident and was to extract her revenge.

James was born in Edinburgh Castle on 19 June 1566. The notion that the baby died at birth and that the future James was a substitute child, perhaps the son of the Earl of Mar, is often repeated, but has little to support it. There is the story of 'The Coffin in the Wall', which supposedly contained a skeleton wrapped in a cloth with a royal monogram; it seems most unlikely and, in his youth, James showed marked physical resemblance to Darnley. In spite of his stormy entrance into the world of sixteenth-century Scotland, the little James prospered.

Mary was partially reconciled to Darnley after the birth, but it is unlikely that they ever cohabited again. Although Darnley did see the new-born prince and Mary pronounced solemnly that the child was his son, she seems to have found her husband repulsive from this time. The Earl of Bedford wrote: 'It cannot be for modesty, nor with the honour of a Queen be repeated what she said of him.'

James was thus descended from Margaret Tudor, through both his father and his mother. Margaret is said to have carried the gene of porphyria, which was to affect future kings. If she did indeed carry such a gene, then James would appear to be a very strong candidate to suffer from the malady.

In 1566, Darnley was strangled at Kirk O'Fields. After this time the medical history of Mary is difficult to follow. She is said to have had a miscarriage of twins on 24 July, conceptions which must have taken place long before she married Bothwell in May. This marriage was never satisfactory. Mary's forces were defeated in 1567 and she was deposed in favour of her little son. Elizabeth I reluctantly conceded to Mary's execution at Fotheringay Castle in 1587.

The young James thus began his career as a king at the age of one. He could never have known his mother, as they never lived together at any time. His reign in Scotland was to last from 1567 to 1603.

As a youth, James seems to have been reasonably healthy. At the age of 13 we see the first signs of his homosexuality in his attraction to Esme Stewart, Lord D'Aubigny, whom he finally created Duke of Lennox and who became a firm favourite.

Years of plot and counterplot followed, until in 1582 an episode known as the Gowrie Conspiracy made James permanently afraid of assassination, to the extent that it is said he wore padded clothes to prevent such an occurrence. James had been hunting near Falkland when he was persuaded by Alexander, brother of the Earl of Gowrie, to ride to Ruthven to interview a man seized in Perth. In Gowrie House the King passed through various chambers which were always locked after he passed, until he came to a small turret room where he was confronted by an armed man. In a struggle, James managed to reach a window and cry 'Treason'. His attendants fought their way in, James was rescued and Gowrie and his brother were killed. What exactly took place is not known, but it seems to have given James a lasting fright.

In 1589 James married the Protestant Princess Anne of Denmark, daughter of Frederick II. He sailed in romantic fashion from Scotland to bring back his bride, who was only 15 at the time, and a lively and very lovely little princess. She was to bear him seven children, but only three were to reach adulthood, which was not unusual at the time.

The eldest boy, Henry, was born five years after the marriage. He was a splendid athletic boy, quick and impulsive, with an excellent brain which made him a very good scholar. He showed brilliant promise and was unimpressed by his somewhat slovenly father. James, however, doted on his son and was an exemplary family man, although he never quite gained his children's confidence and admiration.

The second child, Elizabeth, was two years younger. She resembled her mother in looks and had the same vitality as her elder brother. A third child, Margaret, lived for 15 months. The fourth child, Charles, was born in 1600 and was so weak and sickly that he was baptised at birth. The last three children all died. Perhaps we see here the effect of multiple pregnancies close together, which would have left the mother suffering from chronic anaemia.

The young Charles survived in spite of everything, although at the age of four he could neither walk nor talk. He was placed under the care of Lady Carey and prospered. Anne herself was a very loving mother, and she and James probably gave Charles the experience of a happy family, which was greatly to influence his later life.

In 1589, 1599 and again in 1600, James was making military preparations, showing his determination to use force in support of his claim to the English throne. Between 1600 and 1603, Sir Robert Cecil gave him great support. On 24 March 1603 Elizabeth died and in less than three days Sir Robert Carey had brought the news to James. In a message to his new subjects, James declared: 'I thought to have employed you with armour, now, I employ only your hearts.' He left Edinburgh on 5 April and reached London by 7 May.

At the time of his succession, James was 37 and in good health. He was to survive the Gunpowder Plot of 1605. On 3 November 1612 he was devastated when his beautiful son Henry contracted typhoid and was dead in three days. Charles was now Prince of Wales. In 1613, his daughter Elizabeth married the Elector of Palatine and left England.

James's interests were literature and poetry. He wrote several books and was no mean poet, and the elegant Bible commissioned during his reign is still with us. He had a very harsh attitude to smoking: 'A custom loathsome to the eye, hateful to the nose, harmful to the brain, dangerous to the lungs and in the black, stinking fume thereof, nearest resembling the horrible Stygian smoke of the pit that is bottomless.' Perhaps his chronic chest infection was the reason for his dislike of smoke.

James had the habit of giving favours to young men to whom he had become attracted. Robert Carr rose to become Earl of Somerset, before unfortunately becoming involved in a scandal in 1616 and having to retire from court. In George Villiers James found an excellent replacement, a youth full of grace and with all the social attributes, but with a brain which did not match his physique. James made him a knight of the Garter and created him Earl of Buckingham. James was apt to caress his favourites openly, which did not please his less demonstrative son, Charles. However, Charles himself became very fond of Buckingham.

In 1619 Anne died, after a long illness, suffering from dropsy and renal failure associated with anaemia. James himself was becoming prematurely senile, doting on his 'Baby Charles' with a sickly, cloying affection. Charles turned to Buckingham for friendship, while James became thin and wasted, with a mild fever, possibly caused by chronic fibroid tuberculosis. The possibility of his having porphyria is not very likely as there is no history of any alteration in his urine, a sign which would have been noticed by his physicians. He might well, however, have been a carrier of this genetic condition. Charles was sent off to Spain with Buckingham to find a bride and as he passed through Paris, he saw the sister of Louis XIII, the young Henrietta Maria, who was to become his wife.

Increasingly, James took little part in government and become progressively senile and weak. Never known for clean habits, he washed only occasionally and had a somewhat dishevelled appearance. (In this he was far removed from his son Charles, who was so neat and fastidious in his habits.) James continued to lose weight and his cadaverous appearance became even more marked. His interest in witchcraft and all matters related to the occult also grew. In 1625 London was once again infested with bubonic plague. James and his Court retired to Theobalds near Hatfield in Hertfordshire. Here James became seriously ill. His long-lasting debility may well have been due to chronic fibroid tuberculosis and early in the year, he became affected with recurrent attacks of fever. On occasions he is said to have had 'convulsions'. He realised that his condition was serious and said: 'I shall never see London again.'

So we come to the part played by Buckingham at his death. James had been getting worse and worse, finding no relief from the variety of applications and drinks given him by his physicians. Fortunately for James, the severe remedies later tried for Charles II were not applied in his case. Buckingham then advised a remedy which he had been offered and which was apparently of great medicinal value. He suggested this white powder to James, who at first would not agree to its use. Buckingham persisted and James at last agreed to try it with a little wine. At the same time, he tried a salve given by Buckingham's mother. Unfortunately, the King grew steadily worse. Whether the powder and salve had anything to do with his decline is unclear, but inevitably, as his condition deteriorated, Buckingham and his mother were blamed and even accused of giving the King poison. Buckingham's mother visited James and knelt at his bed, protesting that she was being accused of poisoning him. James cried out: 'Poisoning me!' and fainted from horror. On 25 March he suffered a type of stroke, after which he rapidly deteriorated. He also developed severe diarrhoea, which, coupled with a loss of appetite, would cause dehydration. There are also descriptions of his extremities becoming black and even of his nails falling off, and it was said that his hair stuck to his pillows and came away. Could this have been due to the unfortunate medicine given to him by Buckingham? (It is interesting that the description is very similar to that given at the death of Edward VI.) If the white powder was arsenic, it might well have produced symptoms similar to those described.

The clinical picture at death is probably obscured by the various treatments and by the unreliable descriptions given by writers trying to find culprits for a death which was inevitable. James had reached a state of severe debility brought on by some three years of progressive illness. Chronic fever with loss of weight and appetite had continued over a prolonged time; he coughed and expectorated and salivated to excess, due to a chronic chest infection which was probably tuberculous. The terminal state of superadded bronchopneumonia is common enough and indeed became known as the 'old man's friend'. James may well have died in this way, his last days being marred by arsenic poisoning, perhaps given with good intentions. He thus died of chronic pulmonary tuberculosis complicated by several additional factors.

The young Charles gave his father a very elaborate funeral. After his embalming, James was laid in state in a magnificent manner. His hearse and decorations were designed by Inigo Jones and Charles was the principal mourner, walking alone at his father's funeral as he had done for his mother. James was laid to rest in Westminster Abbey at night, in accordance with the custom that all funerals should take place after dark. After taking such care with the lying-in-state, it is most strange that Charles did not prepare an elaborate tomb in the abbey for his father. During his lifetime, James had brought his mother, Mary, Queen of Scots, to rest in the abbey, where he gave her a tomb to rival that of Elizabeth I. But Charles took no care in regard to the final resting-place of his father.

Having lain in state, the body of James was placed in the abbey tombs, but where, nobody knew for a long time. His body was 'lost'; no record existed of where it had been placed. Such a state of affairs is highly unusual. Eventually, in the reign of Victoria, when the tombs in the abbey were being reviewed and surveyed, James was found to be in the tomb of Henry VII himself, in the Henry VII Chapel. He seems to have been placed there by the gravediggers, who even left their initials to show their work. On whose authority he was placed in the tomb of Henry VII will never be known. Henry and his wife, who lie together, were once again replaced in their tomb and James allowed to lie with them, as he does to this day.

Charles I

◡

Born Dunfermline Palace, 19 November 1600
Executed Whitehall, 30 January 1649

C HARLES was the second son of James I and Queen Anne of
Denmark. Not very robust as birth, he was not expected to live
and was baptised immediately. However, he managed much better
than expected and was sufficiently well to be christened formally
on 23 December as Charles, Duke of Albany and Earl of Ross, the
titles of his grandfather, the Earl of Darnley. On his father's side he
was descended from Henry, Earl of Darnley, who was descended
from Margaret Tudor, sister of Henry VIII, by her second marriage
to the Earl of Angus. Their daughter, Margaret Douglas, married
Matthew Stuart, Earl of Lennox, and their son was Henry, Earl of
Darnley. Mary, Queen of Scots married Darnley and so Charles was
their grandchild.

Charles grew up a very frail boy who was extremely slow in developing. At the age of four he could not walk properly and had a
speech impediment, which he was to retain all his life. The day he
was born was the day on which Gowrie and his brother were killed
during the failed assassination attempt on Charles's father, James I
– such was the atmosphere of violence into which he was born. It
was in the court of his somewhat eccentric father that Charles was
to spend his childhood.

Until he was 11 years old, Charles was under the care of Lady
Carey. Her husband first came to the attention of James when he
rode from Elizabeth's deathbed to acquaint him of the news. James
made Carey a gentleman of the bedchamber and his wife was given

charge of the young Charles. As Charles grew, his father lost patience with his inability to talk and wanted the fraenum of his tongue to be cut. This is the small fold under the tongue which holds it in place, and was often divided in the hope that this would correct speech. Lady Carey had great patience with Charles and persuaded James to leave the child's tongue alone. In the same way, James decided that Charles should have small iron boots fitted to his legs to aid his walking. Again, Lady Carey persuaded James to try more patient and simple methods. As a result, Charles prospered and the weak child astonished many with his mental and physical progress.

When James went south to claim his kingdom, the little Charles was thought to be too weak to undertake the journey and was left in Scotland. By 1604 he was well enough to join his family in England, and in 1605 was created Duke of York. Thomas Murray was appointed as his tutor and Charles was soon proficient in Latin, Greek, French and Italian. He was an excellent scholar with a love of the arts, a trait which he possibly inherited from his mother. (From her he may also have inherited a failure to understand money; she had a vast income, but was always in debt, unable to adjust her way of living.) Charles got on very well with Murray and on his brother Henry's death, when he was created Prince of Wales, he promoted Murray to be his personal secretary. Murray's nephew, who was about the same age as Charles, became his playmate, and was afterwards created Earl of Dysart.

Charles's elder brother, Henry, died of what was probably typhoid. He had a great appetite for fresh fruit, oysters and seafood of all kinds and he seems to have eaten to excess. Henry's doctors tried all the usual terrible treatments: cupping, scarification (puncturing the skin), bleeding, shaving of the head – all to no avail. His death put an end to one who might well have been an excellent king, as he was very intelligent and active, although interestingly he too had an impediment in his speech.

Thus it came about that Charles was to inherit the Crown and all the problems that came with it. His father had always had trouble with money, spending to excess and encountering difficulty in persuading Parliament to finance his lifestyle. Charles was to have even more trouble: his struggle with Parliament and the consequent civil war resulted in his defeat and subsequent trial.

At the age of 48, Charles had been King for 24 years. He had been defeated by the Parliamentarians and his appeal for help from his Scottish subjects led to his detention and subsequent trial. The court which was set to try him was never recognised by Charles as having the authority to question him; he was a king, with a 'divine right' to rule. The sentence of the court was a foregone conclusion.

On Saturday 20 January 1649, Charles was brought from Carlton House to Westminster to face the court, which consisted of some 53 members. Its president, one John Bradshaw, was a Cheshire barrister, who wore a high-crowned beaver hat lined with steel plate to protect him. Charles was conducted to a crimson chair and the proceedings began.

John Bradshaw declared: 'Charles Stuart, King of England, the commoners of England assembled in Parliament being sensible of the great calamities which have been brought upon the nation and according to the duty they owe to God, to the nation, and to themselves, have constituted the High Court of Justice before which you now are brought, and you are to hear your charge, upon which the court will proceed.'

John Cook, a lawyer, then said: 'My Lord, on behalf of the commons of England and of all the people thereof, I do accuse Charles Stuart, here present, of high treason and high misdemeanour.'

At this point, Charles told Cook to stop. Cook took no notice of the King, so Charles rapped him on the arm with his cane to attract his attention. The silver head of the King's cane fell off and rolled onto the floor, an omen if ever there was one. Charles picked it up himself. He proceeded to argue his case very well and demanded to know by what power he was brought to court. He overrode Bradshaw and replied to all the charges so skilfully that the president adjourned the session.

As Sunday was a day of rest, the court met again on Monday 22 January. Charles took the initiative, saying that he was concerned not only with his own case but with '…the freedom and liberty of the people of England; and do you pretend that you will, I stand more for their liberties. For if power without law may make lawes, may alter the fundamental lawes of the kingdom, I do not know what subject he is in England who can be sure of his life, or anything he calls his own.'

Bradshaw tried to maintain the dignity of the court, but to no avail. Charles was once again dismissed and returned to Carlton House. Tuesday brought much the same, with the court retiring to the painted chamber in an effort to guarantee clarity of action. The trial was becoming a disaster. However, Cromwell, his son-in-law Ireton and their party did not mean the King to escape. Accordingly, on Saturday 27 January, the president wore a scarlet robe and sentenced the King: 'The said Charles Stuart, as a tyrant, traitor, murderer and public enemy, shall be put to death, by the severing of his head from his body.'

Charles attempted to speak, but was prevented from doing so. He was hustled from the hall and taken to Carlton House, from where he was transferred to St James's Palace. On Sunday 28 January, Charles made his dispositions, sending away his dogs, as they distracted him. He was allowed to meet his youngest children: his daughter Elizabeth, aged 13, and his son Henry of Gloucester, aged eight. Accordingly he collected his jewellery to give them, retaining only the Garter. He sent a message to the Prince of Wales and a letter to his wife, who waited for news at the Louvre. In the evening Bishop Juxton attended him.

On Monday morning his children were brought to him. He told his daughter to remind her older brother James, Duke of York, that he must now look on their sibling Charles not as a brother, but as the King. He also told them his own death would make him a martyr. He told the little boy that the executioner would cut off his head, which must have been very frightening for one so young. He gave his jewels to the children. Elizabeth was to die herself within one year and the young Henry at the age of 20, in the year of the Restoration.

Charles slept reasonably well during the night and was up at 5 a.m. on the morning of Tuesday 30 January. He was dressed by Herbert, whom he instructed to take great care over his appearance. A large nightcap was provided so that they could stow his hair on the scaffold. He also asked for two shirts, 'by reason the season is so sharp as probably make me shake, which some observers may imagine proceeds from fear'.

Bishop Juxton now arrived and Charles gave him his bible to give to the Prince of Wales, his ring to the Duke of York, which could be manipulated so that it could be both a sundial and a calculator, and his gold watch to the Duchess of Richmond, a daughter of Buckingham. He then took the sacrament.

It was a bitter day, with the ground iron-hard. Charles stepped out across the grass of the park with his jailer, Colonel Thomlinson, on one hand and Juxton on the other. He always walked at a fast pace, and did so as he went from St James's Palace to Whitehall. He had fasted after his communion and undoubtedly expected that the execution would go ahead at once. This was not to be. Parliament had earlier failed to appreciate that as soon as he was dead, his son Charles would automatically be proclaimed as Charles II; a bill therefore had to be passed making it illegal to proclaim the fact. This meant that Parliament was occupied all morning and Charles had to wait with Juxton and Herbert in a ghastly tension until two o'clock.

A knock came on his door and Charles was led through Whitehall and through the Banqueting Hall to one of the elegant windows which had been enlarged. Beyond this was the scaffold on to which Charles stepped with Juxton and Thomlinson. On the scaffold, the executioner, Gregory Brandon, was disguised with false hair and beard; he was well experienced. The block was a mere eight inches high, with staples to secure the prisoner if necessary. Charles 'looked very earnestly on the block and asked if it could be higher'. He was told it could not.

It is of interest to consider the very low block used at this execution. Cromwell and his party did not want any mishap, but had appreciated the practical difficulties associated with an execution. Where there was a high block, as on Tower Green, there was often trouble: a typical case was to follow some years later in the case of the Duke of Monmouth, where several strokes of the axe were necessary to kill the unfortunate man. When the block is high, the head of the prisoner is flexed to receive the blow. This means that the axe cuts through the neck into the lower face and a terrible mess results. If the block is very low, the head must be extended and a blow to the back of the neck will result in the head being cleanly removed. Charles would have to extend his neck to rest on this low block, ensuring a clean and simple execution. The low block was therefore for humanitarian reasons and not to humble the King.

Charles had made notes for his last speech, but there were none who could hear him, as the mass of people were separated from the scaffold by ranks of soldiers. He closed his speech with the comment that he 'died a martyr of the people'. Prompted by the bishop, he then said, 'I die a Christian according to the profession of the Church of England.' He took off his George, giving it to Juxton for the Prince of Wales with the word 'Remember'. Juxton and the executioner then helped him to put his hair in the nightcap. He looked at the little block and asked, 'Is it fast?' 'It is fast, Sir,' the executioner replied. 'Strike', he said, 'when I put my arms out.' He placed his head on the block, but some of his hair came out of the cap and the executioner started to put this back. Charles thought that he was about to strike and said, 'Stay for the sign.' The executioner replied, 'Yes I will an it please your Majesty.'

Charles made the sign and at one single stroke the head was severed from the body. A great groan went up from the people assembled. Many people, most of whom had to pay for the privilege, were able to soak clothes in the blood and even get pieces of blood-soaked wood.

Charles II was immediately proclaimed in Scotland and Ireland. The King's body was embalmed and taken to St James's, where it was displayed for one week; it is said that even Cromwell came and gazed at him. To have buried the body in Westminster Abbey might have given rise to Royalist demonstrations, so on the night of 7 February, the body was draped in black and placed in a royal coach, followed by four coaches bearing the major courtiers. Through the winter night they went, guided by torches, and they came to Windsor on the 8th. His courtiers came to inspect the grave at the chapel where he was to be buried. They objected to the shallow grave which had been prepared and insisted that he be placed in the royal vault. This was occupied by the large coffin of Henry VIII with his wife, Jane Seymour, in a smaller coffin. There was also an empty space which had been left for Catherine Parr, but she had remarried and so was not placed in the royal vault. Charles was therefore placed in her space on the afternoon of 9 February 1649. His coffin was carried by soldiers with four peers carrying the end of the pall. It was carried out from St George's Hall to the Chapel Royal, with snow falling so heavily that the black velvet became all white; Charles had worn white at his coronation 22 years previously. He was placed in the dark vault with the inscription 'King Charles 1649' and he lies here next to Henry VIII.

The body was to rest in peace until 1813, when during the construction of George III's tomb, the workmen accidentally broke through to the vault of Henry VIII. The fact that the tomb was opened was reported to the Prince Regent, who agreed to examine the contents of Charles's coffin in the presence of a royal physician, Sir Henry Halford. The description given is detailed by A. A. Mitchell in *History Today* 1966:

> On removing the pall, a plain leaden coffin, with no appearance of having ever been enclosed in wood, and bearing an inscription KING CHARLES 1648, in large legible characters, on a scroll of lead encircling it, immediately presented itself to the view. A square opening was then made in the upper part of the lid, of such dimensions as to admit, a clear insight into its contents. These were, an internal wooden coffin, very much decayed, and the Body, carefully wrapped up in cere-cloth, into the folds of which a quantity of unctuous or greasy matter, mixed with resin, as it seemed, but had melted, so as to exclude, as effectively as possible, the external air. The coffin completely full; and from the tenacity of the cere-cloth, great difficulty was experienced in detaching it successfully from the parts which it enveloped. Wherever the unctuous matter had insinuated itself, the separation of the cere-cloth was easy, and when it came off, a correct impression of the features to which it had been applied were observed in the unctuous substance. At length, the whole face was disengaged from its covering. The complexion of the skin of it was dark and discoloured. The forehead and temples had lost nothing of their muscular substance; the cartilage of the nose was gone, but the left eye, in the first moment of exposure was open and full, though it vanished almost immediately; and the pointed beard, so characteristic of the period of the reign of King Charles, was perfect. The shape of the face was long oval; many of its teeth remained; and the left ear, in consequence of the interposition of the unctuous matter between it and the cere-cloth was found entire.
>
> It was difficult, at this moment, to withhold a declaration, that, notwithstanding its disfigurement, the countenance did bear a strong resemblance to the coins, the busts, and especially to the pictures of King Charles I by Vandyke, by which it has been made familiar to us. It is true, that the minds of the spectators of this interesting sight were well prepared to receive this impression; but

it is also certain, that such a facility of belief had been occasioned by the simplicity and truth of Mr Herbert's narrative, every part of which had been confirmed by the investigation, so far as it had advanced. It will not be denied that the shape of the face, the forehead, an eye and the beard are the most important features by which resemblance is determined.

When the head had been entirely disengaged from the attachment which confined it, it was found to be loose and without any difficulty was taken up and held to view. It was quite wet, and gave a greenish tinge to paper and linen, which touched it. The back part of the scalp was entirely perfect and had a remarkably fresh appearance; the pores of the skin being more distinct, as they usually are when soaked in moisture; and the tendons and ligaments of the neck were of considerable substance and firmness. The hair was thick at the back part of the head, and in appearance, nearly black. A portion of it, which had since been cleaned and dried, is of a beautiful dark brown colour. That of the beard was of a redder brown. On the back part of the head, it was no more than an inch in length, and had probably been cut so short for the convenience of the executioner or perhaps by the piety of friends soon after death, in order to furnish memorials of the unhappy king.

On holding up the head, to examine the place of separation from the body, the muscles of the neck had evidently retracted themselves considerably; and the fourth cervical vertebra was found to be cut through its substance, transversely, leaving the divided portions perfectly smooth and even, an appearance which could have been produced only by a heavy blow, inflicted with a very sharp instrument, and which furnished the last proof wanting to identify King Charles the First.

And so Charles was returned to his resting place. When this was done, the fourth cervical vertebra, which has been described, was found to be left out, most probably by design. Either the Prince Regent agreed to Sir Henry Halford retaining this as a memento, or Sir Henry retained it without drawing it to the attention of those present. He then had it mounted, to use as a salt cellar.

In 1888, it was returned to the Prince of Wales, who decided, with the permission of Queen Victoria, that it should be restored to the tomb. Accordingly, this was done on 13 December 1888. A small lead and wooden casket was made and was engraved with details of its contents. This was then lowered through a small hole in the floor of the chapel so that it rested on the velvet pall of the coffin.

An article in *The Sunday Telegraph* of 20 September 1987 confirms this and also tells us that in 1813 a workman removed a finger bone from the body of Henry VIII and used it to make a knife handle.

Oliver Cromwell

~

Born 25 April 1599
Died Whitehall, 3 September 1658

He fell sick of a tertian fever which at first seemed not to signify much danger, but by degrees it grew upon him. On Tuesday 31st August, finding himself in danger, he named his son to succeed him. On Friday 3rd of September at three o'clock in the afternoon he departed this life. (From Baker's *Chronicle*)

On opening the body, of the animal parts the cerebral vessels were seen to be more engorged than normal; of the vital, the lungs were somewhat inflamed; but the source of the disease was plain in the natural parts; the spleen although healthy to outward view, yet within contained matter like the lees of oil. (George Bate, physician)

THE QUESTION obviously arises as to whether Oliver Cromwell should be included in a list of the monarchs. He was never actually crowned, although he lived as if he were, particularly in the later years of his life. A somewhat similar debate took place when the placement of statues of the monarchs in Parliament was being considered. The Irish members objected, so the statue of Cromwell was not placed within the House but was erected in Parliament Square, where it now stands. In this position it has attracted more interest and attention than all the others. Perhaps it is fitting that one who did so much for the liberties of his country should be included. His death was not a very memorable affair, but the disposal of his remains, as we shall see at the end of this chapter, is fascinating.

The death of Cromwell was, from a medical point of view, in

some ways similar to that of Charles II, who was to follow him, although two more different characters can hardly be imagined. The austere Cromwell and the dissolute King both suffered from a chronic renal infection, though acquired from very different causes; Cromwell from a bladder stone and Charles from venereal disease.

In adult life, Cromwell had been a tough, hard-riding, military man, reasonably free from sickness. While he was conducting the campaign in Ireland, he had a severe bout of malaria, which was common enough at the time. As mentioned earlier, the type of malarial parasite found in the British Isles at this time was not the virulent tropical type caused by *Plasmodium falciparium*; rather, it was a milder infection caused by *Plasmodium vivax*, which did, however, lead to increasing anaemia, rendering the sufferer prone to any intercurrent infection or illness. This mild form of malaria was widespread and a common cause of debility.

Cromwell received treatment which involved the administration of the bark of the Peruvian quina-quina tree. This in itself may cause toxic effects, contributing to the development of anaemia, and some have thought that this treatment may have been partly responsible for Cromwell's death. The true healing bark is cinchona, or quinine, which was discovered at a later date.

Cromwell also had several attacks of renal infection consequent upon his having a bladder stone. Recurrent mild attacks were evident during the last ten years of his life and the fact that he had recovered from so many led to him to think that he would always recover. A bladder stone forms as the result of bladder infection; the stone itself then leads to further recurrent infection with cystitis and generalised fever. Pain, sometimes severe, is also a consequence. (Samuel Pepys was to suffer from a stone in the bladder; in his case he had it removed, as is described so vividly in his diary.)

In the spring of 1658, the year of his death, Cromwell had not been well. He had been suffering from his stone and was said to have been receiving treatment with opium, which had rendered him very sleepy and caused a loss of appetite. He was also having attacks of vertigo and had developed an abscess on his back, either a simple boil or more possibly a small carbuncle. He had a surgeon, a Mr Boone, to attend to his abscess.

Cromwell also underwent the distress of watching his favourite daughter, Bettie Claypole, become increasingly ill. She was only 29, but she appears to have had cancer of the womb. This progressed to such an extent that by June 1658 she was desperately ill. The condition took a very long time to kill her and for several months Cromwell fretted as he nursed her. She had periods of severe pain and, on 6 August, she died. Cromwell was prostrate with grief and remained so for several days. The funeral was unusual in that Bettie was taken by barge down the Thames, to be laid to rest in Westminster Abbey. She was the only member of the Cromwell family not to be disturbed at the Restoration, for the whereabouts of her tomb had been lost. She was not rediscovered until 1725, when workmen came upon her tomb by accident. She remains in the abbey to this day.

Cromwell seems never to have fully recovered from her death. He made a partial recovery and by 17 August he was able to go out and ride, but his appearance shocked all who saw him. He was witnessed by George Fox, who, on seeing him attended by his guards, wrote: 'And I saw and felt a waft of death go forth against him that he looked like a dead man.' Cromwell himself, however, did not feel that he was about to die and took no steps to name his successor. He placed his faith in God and was, in his final illness, much more optimistic about the outcome than his medical attendants. He was also very fortunate in that he did not receive the severe medical attention given to poor Charles II on his deathbed. Cromwell lay peacefully and even had a short period of seeming recovery.

Meanwhile, little was done to ensure a peaceful succession. Of his two sons, the elder, Richard, was a somewhat slow and retiring person, not one to seek power, while the younger, Henry, was a far more forceful personality who might have made much more of the opportunity for power.

On 17 August 1658, Cromwell became ill with pain in the back and bowels. He was moved to Whitehall and by 24 August was having fits, which were recurrent and of varying severity. His renal condition was terminating in renal failure, a condition of uraemia in which fits are common. He had periods of lucidity, during which he had confidence that he would recover, and dreams, usually of a religious nature. He still had not named a successor.

By 2 September, the council had become more realistic about the outcome and endeavoured to get a statement from him before he died. By this time, he was in a terminally drowsy state; however, the name of Richard was given to him and he was able to show his assent. He then made another partial recovery. That night he was very restless and whispered to Harvey, who gave him his drink: 'It is not my design to drink or to sleep, but my design is to make what haste I can to be gone.'

In the morning of Friday 3 September, the day of his victories at the Battles of Dunbar and Worcester, his condition was such that he was able to speak to those about him. By the afternoon he lapsed into a further coma. At about three o'clock, the Lord Protector died. The cause of death was pyelonephritis resulting in uraemia, complicated by a vesical stone and tertiary malaria.

Dr Bate conducted a post-mortem examination. After this examination, the body was prepared for embalming by professional embalmers. Both the post-mortem and the embalming seem to have been limited. All the viscera are removed at a post-mortem, but the organs outside the peritoneal cavity may not be fully examined if the dissection is not continued to these parts; the kidneys and the bladder may thus escape examination. Certainly, Dr Bate makes no mention of a stone or of the state of the kidneys and bladder. He probably did not make the continued dissection which would have been necessary for such a report, and seems to have been so impressed with his findings in the case of the spleen that he seems to have neglected all else. The middle of the spleen was liquefied, which is not characteristic of malaria, although the spleen is otherwise affected by the disease. The embalmers filled the body cavities with aromatics, removed the brain and then enclosed the body in a wooden coffin. This was placed in a second lead coffin. In spite of this, 'yet the filth broke through them all' and the stench became overbearing, as is typical after death from uraemia. It was found to be necessary to bury the body with all haste and this was done while preparations were made for the official burial ceremony.

A vast lying-in-state was arranged to take place at Somerset House. Four rooms were prepared and arranged for the public to pass through, the first three being filled with objects of state. In the fourth was the great wax image of the Protector. In the first few days this lay like a huge doll, clothed in imperial robes with a large crown above and holding in one hand the orb and in the other a sceptre. The whole was illuminated by four huge candlesticks. After a few days, the lying-in-state was altered, with the wax image now standing upright and the crown placed on the head with the eyes opened. Thus Cromwell was crowned in death; there is no doubt but that this symbolism was deliberate.

Arrangements were now made for the funeral itself to take place and, on 23 November, a huge procession was formed to travel to Westminster Abbey with the effigy in a great hearse. Unfortunately, the dark November day brought a gloom to the abbey. It was freezing cold and no arrangements had been made for either lighting or heating, so the elaborate hearse was left in the chapel without any orations, sermons or other rites. The hearse and its effigy remained in this position for several months, with the public paying to obtain admission.

Along with the restoration of the monarchy in 1660 came the passage of the Bill of Attainder. It was decided that the corpses of Cromwell, Ireton and Bradshaw should be exhumed to suffer the fate of those convicted of treason. The corpses were duly exhumed from the abbey by a mason named John Lewis, who was paid 17 shillings for the task. Cromwell and Ireton had been embalmed and their corpses were in a reasonable state, but that of Bradshaw was in a most unpleasant condition. They were taken to the Red Lion Inn in Holborn to await their fate and the following day they were dragged to Tyburn on hurdles and hung on a triple tree. Bradshaw was hung in the middle; he was obviously considered to be the greatest traitor. Here they remained throughout the day. In the late afternoon they were taken down and the heads were hacked off. It took eight blows to separate Cromwell's head from his body. The headless corpses were then put in a large pit below the gallows at Tyburn, while the heads were taken to Westminster Hall and there stuck on wooden poles tipped with iron, then placed high on display. Here they were to remain until 1684.

There are several accounts suggesting that Cromwell took steps to see that no revenge was taken on him after death. One tells us that the body was taken to the field of the Battle of Naseby and was buried on the field; another that he was taken by boat and buried in the Thames; others that he arranged to substitute his own body for that of Charles I at Windsor, although we know this to be false. It seems most unlikely that Cromwell would think of taking any such evasive action. There is, however, the possibility that the soldiers who guarded the bodies in the Red Lion Inn could have been bribed to substitute another body for Cromwell. Cromwell's daughter, Mary Fauconberg, might have managed this and there is an account of her having a corpse buried at Newburgh Priory, where there is a tomb. This story has not been substantiated, as the owners of the priory have never allowed the tomb to be inspected, even when Edward VII took an interest. It is more reasonable to assume that the headless body lies beneath the ground at Tyburn, near to the present-day Marble Arch.

The fate of the head is of considerable interest. It remained on its spike at Westminster Hall until the beginning of the reign of James II, when it was blown down in a gale. One of the sentinels saw it and recognising it for what it was, put it under his cloak and took it home. His daughter eventually sold it to a Cambridge family, from whom it passed to a drunken actor called Samuel Russell. In about 1780, it was seen by a James Cox, the proprietor of a private museum. He recognised its display value and acquired it for this purpose. He in turn sold it for £230, a very large sum at that time, to three speculators who again exhibited it. From here it passed to a Josiah Wilkinson and so to Canon Wilkinson, who left it in his will to Sidney Sussex College, Cambridge, Cromwell's own college.

The head was exhibited in 1911 before the Royal Archaeological Institute. In the 1930s it was examined by a Dr Mornat and a Mr Pearson. They noted that the head was that of a man of about 60. It had the hole which would have been used for trepanning after death, as was necessary for embalming, and it had been severed from the body after death by a number of strokes. They published their complete findings in *Biometrika* and there seems to be no doubt but that the head is genuine. Sidney Sussex College decided to give the head a proper burial. Accordingly, a plaque has been placed near the chapel entrance, which reads: 'Near to this place was buried on March 25th 1960, the head of Oliver Cromwell, Lord Protector of the Commonwealth of England, Scotland and Ireland. Fellow Commoner of this College 1616–1617.' The exact whereabouts of the head is a guarded secret.

It would appear that one particular has been overlooked. In his post-mortem report, Dr Bate says that the cerebral vessels were seen to be more engorged than normal. This would imply that he had removed the brain for examination, as is usual at a post-mortem examination. For him to do this, he would have made an incision through the scalp across the top of the head from ear to ear. The scalp would then be reflected forwards and backwards, revealing the whole of the top of the skull. The top of the skull would then be removed, in the same way as removing the top of an egg, and the brain extracted. Finally, the skull and scalp would be replaced and stitched closed. From the reports there seems to be no evidence that the skull in question had been so opened. If Dr Bates's report is correct, the head may not be that of Cromwell.

Charles II

⁓

Born May 1630
Died Whitehall, 6 February 1685

THE DEATH of Charles II at the age of 55 brought to an end a reign of protracted debauchery. He was, however, a most popular monarch and at the time of his death he enjoyed the general affection of his people. It is perhaps fortunate that he died as he did, or he might well have lapsed into terminal syphilis, with the consequent general paralysis of the insane. A Protestant all his life, he received the sacrament of the Catholic Church on his deathbed from a priest, Father Huddleston, whom he had met after the Battle of Worcester. Thus he characteristically ensured his salvation from both religious denominations, while also keeping his promise to Louis XIV, from whom he received a pension, that he would embrace the Catholic faith.

As a youth, Charles spent much of his life in Paris. Here he came under the influence of the Duke of Buckingham, a somewhat dissolute personality. He had travelled to Paris via Bristol, Wales, the Scilly Isles and Jersey and it was here that he had what may have been his first sexual experiences. He bedded a certain Marguerite de Carteret, by whom he fathered a son named Charles de la Cloche in 1647, who joined the Society of Jesuits. At this time, Charles was a most attractive youth, 6 feet 2 inches tall with thick black hair, a dark complexion, very dark eyes, a large nose and somewhat ugly mouth.

Soon after this adventure, Charles met Lucy Walter and fell violently in love with her. They first met in England, but their romance continued in Holland. Lucy had gone to The Hague as a Mrs Barlow, the mistress of Robert Sidney, but Charles soon usurped the place of Robert. Somewhere between 9 and 17 July 1648, their son, who was created Duke of Monmouth in 1663, was conceived. The birth of this child came as Lucy approached the menopause and some, probably incorrectly, have tried to say that he was not Charles's son. While Lucy and Charles lived together, Charles was the heir to the throne, but by the time of his son's birth he had become Charles II in exile, an altogether different status. It is possible that he married Lucy, as there is some evidence that a marriage certificate was found by the fifth Duke of Buccleuch at a later date, when it was burnt to avoid complications. Lucy was to die in 1658 of a disease incidental to her profession.

By 1650, Charles's interest in Lucy had passed and he took Lady Shannon to his bed, having a daughter called Charlotte Fitzroy by her in 1651. Two more women were to be his mistress while abroad: firstly Catherine Pegge, by whom he had a son, Don Carlos, then Eleanor Needham, Lady Byron. Pepys says that Lady Byron was the 'Kings seventeenth whore abroad', which suggests that there were several others unnamed. There are no reports of Charles having contracted venereal disease, but the possibility must be considered even at this early stage.

Charles's love life continued with a string of further mistresses. By Catherine Pegge he had a further daughter called Catherine before he married the gentle Catherine de Braganza. It is most ironic that Charles's wife was infertile and that they had no legitimate issue. At the time of his marriage he took Barbara Palmer (Villiers) as his mistress, a woman who was well able to look after her own interests. At that time, Pepys says: 'I find that there is nothing almost but bawdy at Court from top to bottom.'

In 1661 Barbara had a son, possibly not by Charles, who refused to recognise this boy. In 1662 she had another son, who was duly recognised. At or around this time, Barbara also had as her lovers Sir Charles Berkeley, James Hamilton, Lord Sandwich and Henry Jermyn. She even cast eyes on the King's young son, Monmouth. All these associations increase the possibility that Charles contracted venereal disease.

In 1663 Frances Stuart came on the scene as a new mistress and the queen became ill of an unspecified fever. It is possible that she had contracted venereal disease from Charles and was making a very slow recovery, although her case does not appear to have been treated as venereal disease. Barbara Palmer had another son who was born in Oxford, where the court had moved to avoid the plague. It seems that at this time Charles had with him as court physician Dr Frazier, who, according to Pepys, was 'the greatest man at curing the claps'. Many thought that the plague and the Great Fire of London which now struck were sent as a judgement on the dissolute life of the court.

By 1667, the flagging King now had the attentions of Louise de Kéroualle and Nell Gwynn, as well as Barbara, to keep him occupied. Louise was probably a virgin when she met him and carried no risk of disease. Charles seemed to hold Louise in especial regard due to her exalted birth. He confided that she was his greatest love and made special provision for her son, who was created Duke of Richmond at the age of three. He was also made Master of the Horse and a knight of the Garter and High Steward of York.

Nell was a very different medical proposition. She had been the mistress of a certain Charles Hart, a stage manager and from him she was 'brought' by Lord Bathurst, with whom she lived at Epsom. She first met Charles in 1667 and in 1670 they had a son, who became Duke of St Albans. Nell was to die in 1687 from a stroke, possibly due to cerebral vascular disease of a syphilitic origin.

His old flames were not forgotten and one of them, Moll Davies, had a daughter, Mary Tudor, who was to marry the Earl of Derwentwater. A son, James Beauclerk, was born in 1671, but he was to die in Paris at the age of eight from a 'sore leg'. During all this time, Charles continued in reasonable health and showed no gross evidence of syphilis, although he did have a continuing renal infection. Not, apparently, until 1673 did Charles have a severe attack of the 'pox'. He was treated by the renowned Dr Frazier and seemed to recover reasonably well. However, with the treatments available at this time, the disease was not likely to be completely cured. A rash develops in secondary syphilis and this disappears spontaneously as the disease progresses so that the patient may feel that he has been 'cured'. Charles did not keep away from any sexual contact while being treated and he passed the disease on to the unfortunate Louise de Kéroualle, who had a severe attack. She underwent treatment, then moved to Tunbridge Wells for convalescence. She took a very considerable time to recover and possibly never became entirely free from disease.

In his later years, Charles was to meet Hortense de Mancini, the Duchess of Mazarin, a particularly beautiful woman of about 30 who was a well-known courtesan. She was soon added to the list of Charles's mistresses. Charles grew very fond of passing his evenings with one or other of his mistresses, playing cards. He seemed to delight in the 'family atmosphere' of having his ladies in conversation or playing cards together. It was one such evening in February 1685 when Charles was seen by John Evelyn, who has described the scene at Whitehall: 'I can never forget the inexpressible luxury and profanes, gaming and all dissoluteness, as it were total forgetfulness of God, the King sitting and toying with his concubines, [the Duchess of] Portsmouth [Louise de Kéroualle], [the Duchess of] Cleveland [Barbara Villiers] and [the Duchess of] Mazarin [Hortense de Mancini], a French boy singing love songs in the glorious gallery, whilst about twenty of the great courtiers, and other dissolute personas were at basset round a large table, a bank of at least two thousand in gold before them.'

At this time Charles was continuing to suffer from a mild renal infection and was having 'attacks' of uraemic origin. Uraemia is a terminal condition where the kidney function has become so deranged that kidney failure is imminent. He also had an ulcer on his leg, which was giving him considerable trouble. Indeed, when Charles suffered his terminal attack, it was the doctors in attendance to treat his leg who were available to give immediate assistance. Although he had been a very active person, fond of walking, he had become less so, probably prevented by this ulcerated leg. Historically, there has always been great interest in the leg ulcer from which Henry VIII suffered, as it is often thought to be an indication that he had syphilis. The ulcerated leg of Charles has received much less attention, although in his case it probably does indicate that the King had a syphilitic infection.

The party described above by Evelyn was to be the last that Charles attended. On that day, 1 February, he had not been too well, with trouble from his leg preventing him taking his customary walk. Instead he went for a drive. On his return Charles rested and then had his supper. The meal was the usual hearty affair, but also contained the unusual item of two goose eggs, which may well have played a considerable part in the further events. After eating his supper, the King went to the apartments of Louise, where the energetic game of basset described by Evelyn was played. Two other mistresses were present and Charles had a 'family' evening.

He returned alone to his apartments and was put to bed by Bruce, his gentleman-in-waiting, and a certain Harry Killigrew, his groom of the bedchamber. They slept in the bedroom itself. It was noted by Killigrew that the King, who was usually a heavy and undisturbed sleeper, tossed and turned, and at one stage he even called out in his sleep. Perhaps the goose eggs were giving him trouble, for no sooner had he awakened than he went into the privy closet, just off the main closet, which was strictly private. The King remained in this closet for such an inordinate time that Bruce went to find William Chiffinch, the King's keeper of the closet, who alone was able to enter unbidden. Some considerable time was taken in locating Chiffinch and bringing him to the closet. Bruce felt that the King should be wearing more than his nightgown and asked Chiffinch to take in some warmer clothing. At length, as Charles still did not emerge, Chiffinch entered and conducted the King back into his bedroom.

All was not well. Charles was confused, had great difficulty in conducting normal speech, and could not stand unaided. It is very likely that Charles had diarrhoea as a result of eating the goose eggs, which are notorious for being infected. He may even have vomited. This would cause fluid loss and a consequent dehydration, which would have immediately aggravated his uraemic state, itself the result of the inability of his kidneys to excrete the normal toxic product of metabolism. These toxins therefore gradually accumulated in the blood, reaching such a level that a state of mental confusion resulted, associated with fits of deeper unconsciousness. This condition, left untreated, would progress to death. Other symptoms include a dry tongue and offensive breath, with the colour of the patient showing his poor condition. All these were observed in Charles, who was in such a state of confusion that he was unable to attend to the matter of the daily password for his guards. As he became progressively uraemic, he could but say a few disjointed words.

With such a condition, the administration of fluids of any sorts would be beneficial to help excretion. He was given a little sherry and a little China Orange. Both these fluids were helpful (although alcohol would better have been avoided), and he proceeded to have his usual shave. As he had previously suffered similar mild attacks, his attendants did not take immediate drastic steps, feeling that the condition would pass. However, while being shaved, the King suddenly gave out a most piercing cry and sank back into his seat unconscious. He now passed into a state of full uraemic coma. His barber and the attendants were now seriously alarmed and immediately brought into the room one of the King's doctors, who had been waiting outside to enter and attend to his ulcerated leg. This ulcer was either a varicose ulcer or possibly a syphilitic gumma. Whatever the case, the medical men had been unable to heal it and it had become offensive. Sir Edmund King, the doctor who now attended, recommended that bleeding take place urgently and with the leave of Bruce, he proceeded to bleed the King, removing some 16 ounces of blood.

Unfortunately for Charles, a group of medical men was immediately summoned and advised an assortment of remedies. The Privy Council was also urgently summoned. At this time, medical knowledge and treatment was limited. Medicine was not secured on any scientific basis, although Charles had himself founded the Royal Society. Treatment had hardly changed since the time of Galen and the doctors now set about using all the usual antique methods on the unfortunate King. His head was shorn and he was bled once again, this time 8 ounces being removed. He was given cantharides (Spanish fly) as a blistering agent. In spite of this, his speech improved somewhat in the course of two hours.

The King's brother, the Duke of York, sat with Charles, who improved far enough to be able to hold some conversation. Indeed, given the previous mild attacks, his brother now thought that Charles might recover. Steps were taken to see that no message of the King's illness be taken abroad, specifically to the Duke of Monmouth or to William of Orange; as a reasonable precaution the ports were closed. Charles now passed through a period of alternating improvement and decline. On Tuesday 3 February he had a further fit or convulsion, which stimulated the doctors to even greater efforts. By now he had 12 doctors in attendance and they renewed their activity.

The list of the medicines used is truly astonishing: plasters of Burgundy pitch and spurge were applied to the feet, plasters of cantharadine applied to the head; white hellebore root was used as a sneezing agent; enemas of rock salt, of syrup of buckthorn and of orange infusion of metals in white wine were given; also medicines of cowslip infusion, vitriol in paenony water, spirit of sal ammoniac, julep of black cherry water, oriental bezoar from the stomach of an eastern goat and spirits of human skull. In all, some 58 drugs were administered in the course of five days.

Under this treatment the uraemia progressed and his condition gradually worsened. Broth and posset were given from time to time and these would have been helpful, but the use of impossible medicines continued. It seems that as Charles revived, the medical men thought of more and more painful remedies to keep him from lapsing into unconsciousness. Hot irons were applied to the King's head and to his feet, while cupping glasses were also used. The poor King underwent a very great trial and it is an indication of his reasonable nature that there is no record of his having complained. It could never be said that the doctors were not trying.

Charles was also given Peruvian bark of cinchona, which has led some to think that he might have had malaria, but there is nothing further to support such a possibility. As some of the would-be remedies involved the use of mercury, mercurial poisoning has been postulated as a contributing factor to his death. While this is a remote possibility, there is nothing more to support evidence of any form of poisoning other than the two goose eggs so well documented. There seems to be no doubt that the main condition was progressive uraemia, or chronic renal failure, probably aggravated by the treatment given. The irritant cantharades would most certainly have hindered any possibility of recovery.

Throughout all this time, the chamber had been full of people: never was there a more public deathbed. The queen had been with him, but was taken away as she was near collapse. After some time, Louise was allowed to enter and she removed two very large diamond rings from Charles's fingers. She was observed by the Duke of York, who is reputed to have said: 'They are as safe in your hands as in mine.'

As the condition progressed, the several bishops present read prayers. It was at this point that Charles embraced the Catholic faith and received the sacrament. His brother, James, was always a staunch Catholic and after whispered talk with him, it was decided to bring Father Huddleston into the chamber. Great care had to be exercised, as it was still a crime to be a Catholic priest and several priests had been prosecuted in recent times. Huddleston was brought in and admitted the King into the Catholic faith. He had at last honoured his agreement with Louis XIV that he would embrace Catholicism. Absolution was given and he received the sacrament, but still Charles did not die, although he was now having great difficulty in speaking.

His trials continued throughout Thursday 5 February. He was again 'treated' by his doctors, and more blood was removed. Charles was intermittently conscious and comatose. He had a long conversation with his brother, the Duke of York, regarding the welfare of his family. He talked of his wife and of Louise, and uttered the well-known phrase 'Let not poor Nellie starve'. He asked for the clocks in his room to be wound up. At dawn he had the curtains drawn back so that he might see the sunrise over the Thames. At about 8.30 a.m. he slowly passed into deepening coma and he died at noon on Friday 6 February 1685.

How far the death of Charles can be ascribed to his venereal disease cannot be estimated. There seems to be little doubt that he was dying from chronic renal failure.

A death mask, taken at the time, provides the face for the effigy still to be seen in Westminster Abbey. It expresses quite vividly the suffering of his deathbed.

Charles's burial was not a grand affair, although it might well have been thought that the popular King would have had a very splendid funeral. Like all burials, it took place after dark. James II did not bother to attend, perhaps because Charles was buried in the Protestant faith. This might also account for the smallness of the ceremony. Charles was buried in a plain vault in the Henry VII Chapel in Westminster Abbey. In 1867, the vault was opened while new heating pipes were fitted. It was noted that his lead coffin was much corroded and collapsed and that the King's remains were visible. In 1977, when the vault was again opened, the remains were still visible.

It is of interest to note that on his restoration Charles II decided to arrange for a suitable tomb for his father and grandfather. He was unable to do either of these things, as it was not known where in the abbey James had been interred. And although Charles I was known to have been in St George's Chapel, Windsor, there was no exact record as to where the body had been placed. Accordingly, no action was taken.

James II

〜

Born St James's Palace, 15 October 1633
Died St Germain, 16 September 1701

On march 4th, he fainted away, but that day evening being seized again with a paralytic fit as he was dressing it so affected one side that he had difficulty to walk and lost the use of his right hand, but after blistering he walked fairly well. On July 13th he had another fit. On September 2nd he was seized again and fell into another fit two days later was for some time without life or motion till his mouth being forced open he vomited a great quantity of blood. The doctors gave him kinkinna and blistered him in several places which gave him great torment. The next day he continued lethargic and two days later grew much weaker, was taken with continual convulsions or shaking in the hands, and the day following being Friday 16th September about three in the afternoon, he died. (J. S. Clarke, from *Life of James II*)

JAMES'S PARENTS, Charles I and Henrietta Maria, were a rare royal couple in that they appear to have been in love during the births of their family. Their first child was premature and died, but they went on to have Charles (later to become Charles II) in 1630, Mary in 1631 and James, Duke of York in 1633.

James was a very attractive child with fair hair and blue eyes, very different from his elder brother who was very dark with a large nose and a somewhat unattractive mouth. He became a most pleasant youth, good-looking and easy in his manner. Although he was brought up as a staunch Protestant, his early life was filled with the pleasures provided by the court of his father, Charles I. In later life, he was to play second string to his elder brother for 52 years before he began his short reign.

The pleasure and the freedom of the early years of Charles's reign were soon marred by the onset of the civil war. James was in Oxford for most of this time, observing the passing phases of the contest but taking no active part, being too young. Finally, in 1645, he was sent to Hull to secure the city, but he was unable to do anything constructive and defeat and humiliation followed. In 1646, the city of Oxford fell and James found himself a prisoner under Percy, Earl of Northumberland. He was held at Hampton Court, but managed to escape, disguised as a girl. He fled to France to join the court in exile and for three years the young James lived among all its despair and intrigue. Then in 1652 he joined the army of the French King. He proved to be a most able soldier, learning under the great Turenne, and rose to become a lieutenant-general. However, Cromwell at this time made a truce with the French and they agreed that a number of Cavaliers could not find refuge in France. James had to leave and he decided to join the Spanish cause. At the Battle of the Dunes, he showed himself to be a decisive and gallant soldier and it is noteworthy that by 1660 he was so well regarded that he was offered the post of High Admiral of Spain, an appointment usually reserved for members of Spanish royalty.

On the restoration of his brother to the throne, James returned to England and in May 1660 he was appointed Lord High Admiral of the English fleet. He was now part of the dissolute court of his brother and he took to the life with gusto. James was just as bad as his brother, revealing a hitherto suppressed side of his character. He could not resist the ladies of the court and seems to have 'specialised' in those who were not of an attractive appearance. He soon impregnated Anne Hyde, the daughter of the chancellor. He then committed what was thought to be a great faux pas in marrying her, something he felt obliged to do, having signed a marriage proposal with her when he had been an unimportant soldier of fortune, rather than the brother of the King. James and Anne married in private on 3 September 1660 and their child, Charles, Duke of Cambridge, was born on 22 October. The baby died of smallpox that winter, as did James's brother Henry and his sister Mary.

James had two recreations which he pursued with great determination: hunting and women. He courted many of the beauties of the Restoration, but finally fell in love with Arabella Churchill, sister to John Churchill, who was to remain one of his mistresses until 1678.

As Lord High Admiral, James devoted himself to the rebuilding of the navy, but he found the Dutch more than a match for his efforts; the English and Dutch were rivals in fishing and trade. When the Dutch founded settlements on the Hudson River in North America among the English colonies, the merchants appealed to Parliament and war was declared. James secured victory at the Battle of Lowestoft, but his great friend Berkeley was killed while standing next to him. James slept after the battle, so failing to follow up his advantage, which is possibly an early sign of his altering character. Plague and fire now fell upon London and the Dutch fleet was able to enter the Medway in 1667 and burn much of the English fleet.

In view of the number of women he took to his bed, James may well have contracted venereal disease at this time, or even at an earlier date. We know that he had a definite attack of syphilis contracted from Anne, Countess of Southesk. He was probably treated by Dr Frazier, who had treated Charles when he suffered from this terrible disease. Not only does the disease itself spread through the body and damage the nervous and vascular systems, but the treatments used at that time, particularly mercury, must also have had a most toxic effect. James was slowly to fall victim to the disease and there was a marked alteration in his character and ability.

A second great change came over James when he converted to the Catholic faith and, like so many converts, he became even more intense in his religion than many of a longer-standing faith. In spite of this he continued to have a succession of mistresses, once admitting, 'I less than any other can say I have lived up to what I professed since I was reconciled.' He became somewhat withdrawn and morose and Nell Gwynn apparently called him 'Dismal Jimmy'.

Mary and Anne, his two daughters by Anne Hyde, were born before he contracted syphilis. In March 1671, Anne Hyde died and soon afterwards James married Mary of Modena, a staunch Catholic, who was thought incapable of bearing a normal child. During Charles's reign, the Catholic plots, particularly that of Titus Oates, nearly destroyed James, but he was able to prove his innocence of a plot against his brother. Nonetheless, a Bill of Exclusion was brought before Parliament to exclude the possibility of a Catholic becoming king; it was defeated, which was a triumph for James. Then in February 1685, Charles died.

The new King was recognised to have certain excellent attributes. He was a sober individual, never having been one for alcoholic excess and he tended to drink fruit drinks. He was a hard-working individual with an ability for detailed administration. James was also honest and loyal to his friends, but he had become a devout Catholic and did not hide the fact that he celebrated Mass. In this respect, at least, he was honest. However, he continued to have a succession of ladies creeping up the back stairs of the palace. He now took Catherine Sedley for mistress in succession to Arabella Churchill. Catherine was a Protestant and it was hoped, incorrectly, that she might influence James.

Although unpopular, James was getting old and many thought that with the accession of his daughter, Mary, the country would soon be relieved of the Catholic menace. They were willing to wait for the new times and no effort was made at home to displace James.

This 'wait and see' policy was to suffer a rude shock when in 1688, Mary of Modena became pregnant. It had been thought that she would never have a child, as six previous pregnancies had resulted in two miscarriages, three children who died in their first year and a fourth who died at the age of four. Now she was pregnant again and for some reason the Catholic party felt that on this occasion they would have a male heir. The birth took place at St James's Palace and was attended by the rumour of the 'warming pan', in which a child was said to have been smuggled into the room and then brought in for display. Was there such a substitution? Although much was made of this by the Protestants, it seems unlikely that the child who was to become James, the Old Pretender, was not the son of James II, born on 20 June 1688. The birth altered the whole political scene, since James now had a successor. The subsequent trial of seven Protestant bishops was to make the King's unpopularity even more marked.

The Protestant William of Orange was invited to invade England and replace James and this is what he did, landing at Torbay. This is when the alteration which had taken place in James becomes most evident. It is possible that he was suffering from cerebral vascular disease following syphilitic infection. Certainly, he who had been such a good soldier and so decisive in his youth now delayed taking any decisive action against William. He finally moved to meet his challenger and reached Salisbury, where he was confined to his rooms with a severe nosebleed. As he waited, he received a succession of bad news: his troops in the north were defeated; his second in command, Lord Churchill, deserted with a considerable number of persons; and his own daughter, Mary, declared against him. James could either negotiate, fight or flee. He chose the last and so left the field clear for William.

Unfortunately, he could not even flee with any success. He was recaptured and brought back to London. Here he was well received and might well have made a reasonable effort to retain his throne, but again he decided to flee. This time he was successful, reaching the continent on Christmas Day 1688. James was to try once more to regain the throne through a campaign in Ireland, the Battle of the Boyne in July 1690, but here again he had to watch his forces being defeated.

For the rest of his life, devotion occupied his time, and he was obsessed with his salvation. It became difficult to interest him in any other matter. He frequented the Convent of La Trappe, where total silence was observed. His visits were interspersed with fasting, prayer and self-imposed penances, including the wearing of an iron chain studded with sharp points. He still pursued his great love of hunting and even at the age of 66 he was able to ride well, in spite of his increasing infirmity.

In August 1701, while he was hearing Mass, James suffered a cerebral thrombosis resulting in a right-sided hemiplegia, or paralysis. He partially recovered from this, as is not unusual, only to have further attacks which were characterised by varying degrees of unconsciousness and paralysis. Syphilitic cerebral vascular disease would account for these symptoms, and for his altered mental attitude in later life, his indecision and his general mental decline. The condition was possibly also associated with hypertension, as he had been having nosebleeds. We are told that he had a large vomit of blood forced from his mouth, which might have been due to a leaking syphilitic aneurysm, but the direct cause of his death was no doubt due to cerebral vascular thrombosis. As James lay dying, he said to his devoted queen: 'Think of it, madam, I am going to be happy.' The poor King had known little happiness since he came to the throne.

He died on 16 September 1701 at St Germain.

Mary II

～

Born St James's Palace, 30 April 1662
Died Kensington Palace, 29 December 1694

M ARY WAS born the second child of Anne Hyde, wife of James II. There was not the fuss and celebration which would usually follow the birth of a child to the Duke of York, as James had married Anne Hyde under somewhat unusual circumstances. As a young soldier James had contracted a marriage with Anne, but before it could be implemented his brother became King. James was now Duke of York, and all felt that he would break his contract, but he decided to honour it, knowing that Anne had become pregnant. Accordingly they were married and their first child was born, to live for only a few days. Mary was the child of the second pregnancy, and she was followed by a second girl, Anne.

Mary was a very happy child, full of fun and chatter, who enjoyed playing cards from an early age. She was so different from her sister that the Duchess of Marlborough described them thus: 'It was indeed impossible they should be very agreeable to each other because Mary grows weary of anybody who would not talk a great deal and Anne was so silent that she rarely spoke more than was necessary to answer a question.'

As a child, Mary was her father's favourite. She took part in court masques and there is a delightful painting of her at an early age by William Wissing. Her mother, Anne, was unable to stop James from his infidelities and took to eating a great deal. She became very obese before she died, most probably from breast cancer. Mary was brought up in the strict Protestant faith. Her youth-

Anne's husband, George, accompanied William on his campaign in Ireland, but was denied any command and was even denied social contact with the senior officers of William's army. William also refused to promote Churchill, the husband of Anne's best friend, Sarah. When Anne appealed to Mary with Sarah in attendance, Mary was furious and a quarrel ensued, both sisters attacking each other in such a way as to make the possibility of reconciliation very difficult. Indeed, the two never met or spoke together again. This behaviour was most unlike Mary, who was generally easy-going and warm. William continued to barely tolerate George, whom he regarded as a lazy fool, and this may well have influenced Mary's opinion. Many efforts were unsuccessfully made to bring the two sisters together; the clockmakers of the time even put figures of both of them together on clocks to promote friendliness, but to no avail.

It was now December 1694 and Mary must have been feeling none too well. She had lost some of her usual vivacity and complained of tiredness; she also took great pains to get all her affairs in order, going through her papers and destroying those she did not wish to be found. On 20 December she fell ill, with an increasing fever, and by 22 December her condition was giving rise to anxiety. Her doctors at once diagnosed smallpox. This was a great shock to William, whose parents had both died from this disease. Accordingly he 'burst into tears and cried out that here was no hope of the Queen and from being the happiest he was going to be the miserablest creature upon earth'. He moved into Mary's room, sleeping on a camp bed. It must be remembered that William had suffered an attack of smallpox previously and it was appreciated that he was not likely to have a further attack. William found the atmosphere of the sickroom very difficult with his asthma and breathing difficulties, and Mary was only upset by his continual weeping and his general attitude.

By the 28th she seemed to be very much better. Indeed, the doctors began to think that she had perhaps had an attack of measles. Then, during the night of the 28th, her condition suddenly deteriorated. She herself said that she felt little pain and did not feel ill, but she developed several large pustules which suppurated and she also spat blood and produced bloodstained urine. Many dark-coloured

ful companion was Francis Apsley, who may have assumed the role of 'mother', and to whom Mary showed great affection.

Her diplomatic marriage to William could not possibly have been attractive to her. At the time she was 15 years old, no less than 5 feet 11 inches tall, handsome, well dressed and with a beautiful complexion. William was 37, 4 inches shorter than her, pale and ill-dressed, usually in black; he spoke English with difficulty and had constant trouble from his asthma. It is no surprise to learn that Mary was in tears on the day of her wedding. Anne was unable to attend, since she was suffering from a mild attack of smallpox, and as events transpired it is a great pity that she did not give this less virulent form of the disease to Mary.

After the wedding, Mary had to go to the continent with her husband, where William spent most of his time on campaign. However, their relationship slowly improved until Mary was able to lavish affection on her husband, who returned it with reserve.

William was always attracted by handsome young men such as his cousins, and particularly by William Bentinck, who had shown his affection by even sleeping in William's room when he had a mild attack of smallpox in 1675. James II did not get on well with his son-in-law and relations between them became very strained. This may in part have been because James gave Anne a generous allowance but gave nothing to Mary.

Relations between Mary and William were also strained when he had an affair with Elizabeth Villiers, in circumstances which were somewhat unusual, possibly not even sexual. William was nonetheless infatuated with her and continued the relationship after the death of Mary, and even after Elizabeth had married Lord Hamilton. Mary became pregnant, but her child died at birth and the strain of this pregnancy seems to have prevented her from becoming pregnant again.

After she and William assumed the British throne, it was necessary for them to come and live in England. This did not suit either of them: Mary had become very fond of the Dutch people and countryside and they both found English court life irksome. William, in particular, did not fit in well with the demands of this life; Mary managed to spend much of her time on building projects.

Her relationship with her sister Anne now became estranged.

areas of extravasated blood appeared on her body, and her face became very swollen. She started to show the signs of a severe malignant attack of smallpox. She progressively weakened and at about one o'clock in the morning she died.

Walter Harris, writing in 1742 in his *Observations on Certain Grievous Diseases*:

> She took Venice treacle the first evening, and finding no sweat appearing as usual, she took the next morning a double quantity of it before she asked the advice of her physicians. The smallpox was of the very worst and most dangerous sort, being united with the measles as such as it usually accompanied with the erysipelas in the face, pustules and spitting of blood. On the third day of the illness her eruption appeared, with very troublesome cough and they came out in such a manner that the physicians were very doubtful whether they would prove the smallpox or measles. On the fourth day the smallpox showed itself in the face and rest of the body under its proper and distinct form. On the sixth day in the morning the various pustules all over her breast were changed into the large red spots of the measles. And the erysipelas called "rosa" swelled her whole face, the former pustules giving place to them. That evening many broad and round petechiae appeared in the forehead above the eyebrows and on the temples. About the middle of the night there began a great difficulty in breathing and a little afterwards a copious spitting of blood. On the seventh day, the spitting of blood was succeeded by bloody urine. On the eighth day the broad spots of the measles continued on her breast, but in the lower limbs where there had been many pustules of the smallpox all the swelling of them immediately disappeared and they changed into round spots about the bigness of the pustules, of a deep red or full scarlet, their surface being smooth and not at all elevated like the penitential stigmata. There was one large round pustule filled with matter having a broad scarlet circle round it like a burning coal which I then observed above the region of the heart and under her body. Lastly about the middle of the night she breathed out her pious soul.

This gives a very good description of a severe case of smallpox. The possibility of her suffering from a superadded case of measles does not appear to be relevant.

Mary left a note to say that her body was not to be opened. This was perhaps optimistic, as the bodies of royalty were always embalmed before burial, which requires the body being opened. As in the case of Elizabeth I, Mary's body was embalmed after opening. On 5 March she had a very magnificent funeral costing over £50,000, a stupendous sum at that time. William, as is the custom for a monarch, did not attend in person.

Mary was only 32 when she died. She had been a somewhat simple person who had no enemies and was universally loved and respected. She had supported William throughout their marriage, and enabled him to use his talents to the full while she performed the social and ceremonial duties they so much disliked. Being a daughter of James II, she gave continuity to the Crown. Like so many women of her period, she had found it impossible to produce an heir, although her health seems to have been reasonably good prior to her final illness. The pity was that she did not contract a mild form of smallpox at the time when her sister and other members of the court were infected.

William was prostrate with grief at her death.

William III

~

Born 4 November 1650
Died Westminster, 8 March 1702

A L L   T H R E E of the first Williams died by accident. Both
William I and William III, two kings who could hardly have
been more different physically, were killed in accidents associated
with horse riding.

William III was the son of Mary, daughter of Charles I, and her husband William II, Prince of Orange. When Mary reached full term,
her husband contracted a severe attack of smallpox and was dying
as she went into labour, so the event of William's birth was marred
by tragedy. The Prince of Orange had given great support to the
Stuart cause, and both Charles I and Charles II held him in high
regard, while Mary was a favourite sister of Charles II. She wanted
her son to be called Charles, after his uncle, but her mother-in-law,
Anette, was a very determined character and insisted in a fierce
quarrel that the baby be called William, a good Dutch name. So
fierce was their quarrel that when William came to be christened
Mary did not attend.

The young prince was to grow up in the relative quiet of the
Netherlands, a member of the ruling family which had united the
provinces. He was very popular and everywhere he went he was
received with cheers, so that he came to assume that he had almost
a royal standing. He was, however, a very shy youth, small, thin and
pale. As he grew up he developed what is known as an adolescent
kyphosis, or a mild hunchback, so that he walked with his head
pushed forward. Early in life he also developed a recurrent asthma,
which was associated with a hacking cough. Crowded rooms and a

stuffy atmosphere were therefore to be a great trial to him and he always tried to avoid them. He ate sparingly and, in his early days, drank little or no alcohol. He found it difficult to follow English if spoken rapidly. He learnt to control his visible emotions and he very rarely lost his temper or showed other emotions in public. He much preferred the company of his Dutch friends to any other.

William received a good education and was a reasonable scholar, but he was particularly fond of all matters military and he became quite a gifted general. In his early life he had no severe illness, but his health was unfortunately always poor due to his asthma.

In 1660 William's life was changed when his uncle, Charles II, suddenly became King of England. His mother, Mary, went over to England to take part in the general rejoicing, but unfortunately developed smallpox and died. William was now left with little English influence in his life and he drew more into the circle of his Dutch friends and cousins, particularly William Bentinck. William himself developed an attack of smallpox and was cared for by his friends, including Bentinck, who moved his bed into the patient's room. William recovered and the friendship was even closer.

Dutch and English rivalry now developed to the point of war, but it was with the French that William became obsessed. He hated the French and spent much of his life trying to counteract French interests; it is quite possible that he was to see his later association with England as a means of drawing England into the struggle against France.

The possibility of a marriage to Mary, daughter of James II, had been considered for some time. At first William did not further the matter, as James was a devout Catholic and unlikely to ascend the throne. By 1677, however, it was agreed that the marriage should take place and accordingly they married on his birthday, 4 November. Mary is said to have wept throughout the ceremony, although the marriage became more satisfactory with the passage of time. Mary grew to love Holland and William was happy enough with his constant campaigning and hunting. Mary openly admired her husband, but William seems always to have been a very restrained person, who gave a number of presents to his wife, but who showed affection with marked reserve.

He continued to pass much of his time in masculine company, and the possibility of homosexual inclinations cannot be excluded. There is also the matter of William's somewhat strange affair with Elizabeth Villiers, a maid-in-waiting to his wife. It is often said that the friendship was on an intellectual rather than on a sexual plane, but be this as it may, Mary heard rumours and spied on William. She found him coming from the maid's rooms in the night and a long period of coolness developed between them. They became reconciled when Mary discussed the possibility of becoming Queen and told William that he would be more than her consort, as she wished him to reign in equal right. This pleased William greatly and was a great factor in their reconciliation.

In 1688, with the flight of James, following the invasion by William, they were to find themselves joint rulers. Naturally, they now had to live in England and this did not suit either of them. The damp air of England did not help William's asthma, but he found life at Hampton Court more agreeable than in central London. However, there is no record of him having any major illness at this time. In December 1694, Mary developed smallpox and died. William was devastated and took some time to recover.

In accordance with an Act of Parliament, it was decided that if William himself had heirs, then they would inherit the crown. William showed no wish to remarry, although given his and Mary's quarrels with Anne he could hardly have relished the crown passing to her.

The period of 1688–1702 was one in which William spent his time in attending to affairs of state and hunting at Windsor and Richmond. His health gradually became worse with a loss of energy and recurrent swelling of the legs. His breathing also became more difficult, which might well indicate that he was suffering from a mild cardiac incompetence. He began to eat more than he had been accustomed to and also to drink occasionally in public. There is no doubt that he drank in private, particularly at the late evening parties he had with his intimate friends, in the privacy of his own apartments. He became gloomier and very irritable.

William was now living in a very male environment and in 1691 he formed an attachment to a certain Arnold Joost van Keppel, one of his pages. He was a very attractive-looking person, youthful and fresh, and it soon became obvious that he was replacing Bentinck who had been William's 'friend' for so long. Relations between these two became very antagonistic. It was now openly whispered that William was becoming more homosexual. William in turn complained that it was a sorry state of affairs when he was unable to have a close male friendship without being considered homosexual. Whether he was homosexual or not cannot now be proved one way or the other; at the time, homosexuality was not common, at least not in public. Today it might well be assumed that he was of course homosexual, but the matter is open to speculation. William does seem to have been very undersexed in his relationships with women and his constant friendships do seem to indicate homosexual inclinations. He made Keppel the Earl of Albemarle in 1696, which was greatly resented by Bentinck, who had been made Earl of Portland many years before. Both acted as 'confidential personal assistants' to the King.

At the end of 1701 and in early 1702, William's health began to deteriorate. The swelling of his legs was causing considerable trouble and his irritability and breathlessness became more marked. In February he was to suffer an accident which is described vividly in *The Life of William III*, 1706:

On February 21st, riding out from Kensington to Hampton Court as he was putting his horse to the gallop the horse fell, and his majesty in falling broke his right collarbone. Upon this fatal accident his Majesty was carried to Hampton Court, where the bone was dextrously set by Monsieur Ronjat, Sergeant Surgeon to the King, who, having felt his Majesties pulse, told him it was feverish, and that any other person in his condition would be let blood. "As for that" replied the King, "I have now and then had an headache and some shivering fits this afternoon, and this very morning a pain in my head before I went out a hunting". In the afternoon, the King finding himself easy, contrary to advice, returned to Kensington and slept almost all the way in his coach. He came to Kensington at about 9 o'clock at night with his right arm tied up and as he entered the great bed-chamber he saw Dr Bidloo, who finding his pulse in good order dissuaded him from bleeding and after viewing the affected part, gave his majesty to know that the right channel bone was broken obliquely a little below its junction with the shoulder-blade. It was well set, but the jolting of the coach and the loosening of the bandages had occasioned that dis-union. After the fracture was taken care of, his Majesty went to bed and slept the whole night so sound that the gentlemen who sat with him said they did not hear him complain so much as once. His Majesty seemed in a fair way of doing well till Sunday March 1st, a defluxion fell upon his right knee, which was a great pain and a weakness to him and thought to be a very ill symptom.

On Wednesday March 4th, His Majesty seemed so well recov-ered of the lameness in his knee that he took several turns in the gallery at Kensington, but at length, finding himself tired and faint, he sat down on a couch and fell asleep, which probably occa-sioned that shivering fit which soon after seized him and turned to a fever accompanied with vomiting and looseness. The physicians administered several remedies to his Majesty that gave him great relief and he continued indifferently well until Friday 6th when his vomiting and looseness returned so violent upon him that he refused to take any sustenance till 2 o'clock on Saturday morning when he supped a cupful of chocolate that stayed with him; soon after they gave him a gentle sleeping draught to compose him which had that good effect that he rested for three hours after; in the forenoon, he supped some broth and a cordial and found him-self easier although excessively weak. On Saturday night he took some of Ralways cordial with the cordial julep and soon after, some hot claret. About three o'clock on Sunday morning he called again Dr Bidloo and complained to him that he had had a bad night and could not sleep; upon that he sat up and in this posture, he slept for about half an hour and when he awaked said, "You can bear me up no longer." Then he was held up by Dr Freeman on the right and Mr Swell on the left, both of them having pillows in their arms. After seven o'clock he took Bidloo by the hand and breath-ing with great difficulty asked him "If this could last long" again by the hand saying "I do not die yet, hold me fast". Having taken little of the cordial potion, he faintly enquired for the Earl of Portland. About eight o'clock His Majesty sitting on his bed in his night gown and in the arm of Mr Sewell, one of the pages of the bed-chamber, he leaned a little backward towards the left, and shutting his eyes, expired with two or three short gasps.

Two days later, the royal body was opened and the physicians and surgeons summoned by the Privy Council to assist at and examine the dissection made a report:

Upon the viewing the body before dissection the following appearances were remarkable; the body in general was much emaciated; both the legs up to the knees and a little higher as also the right hand and arm as far as the elbow were considerably swelled. There was also on the left thigh near the hip a bladder full of water, as big as a small pullets egg, resembling a blain. Upon opening the belly the guts were found of a livid colour and the blood contained in the vessels black. The gut called ileon had in some places the marks of a slight inflammation. The stomach, pancreas, mesentery, liver, gall-bladder, spleen and kidneys were all sound and without fault. In the thorax or chest, we observed that the right side of the lungs adhered to the pleura and the left much more so; from which upon separation there issued forth a quantity of purulent or frothy serum.

The upper lobe of the left lung and the part of the pleura next to it were inflamed to a degree of mortification and this we look upon as the immediate cause of the King's death. From the ventricles of the heart and the great blood vessels arising out of them were taken several large tough flesh like substances of the kind called polypus. The heart itself was of the smaller size but firm and strong. Upon laying bare the right collar bone, we found it had been broken near the shoulder and well set. Some extravasted blood was lodged above and below the fracture. The brain was perfectly sound and without any sign of distemper. 'Tis very rare to find a body with so little blood as was seen in this; there being more found in his lungs than in all the parts beside put together.

This provides a very vivid picture of a small and frightened man who, having had an accident, is anxious to get back to his home at Westminster. This he did in spite of the uncomfortable coach ride, which may well have disturbed his fracture. He was already suffering from some degree of cardiac failure and the fracture of the collarbone accentuated a lung condition associated with his long-lasting asthma. An inflammation of the lung leading to pneumonia, with infection in the pleural space (empyema), followed, and caused even more distress in breathing. The King now needed to sit upright as he struggled for breath and he was supported by his attendants. He sent for his old friend Bentinck, now Earl of Portland, and the two grasped hands. Portland was very upset at seeing the King and retired in great distress. The only friend the dying King now had was his doctor. Anne, George and his other relatives did not attend. He anxiously asked for support from the doctor and hoped that his struggle for breath would not be too long. Around his neck he wore a cord on which was a ring given to him by Mary and he also had a lock of her brown hair in a small locket. Both were removed on his death.

It is most likely that William had a terminal embolism. This is a clot which becomes detached and passes through the blood vessels, reaching the heart, where it is pushed into the vessels going to the lungs. These are blocked by the clot which in William's case seemed to the physicians to be a solid mass (they say a 'polypus'). The clot also accounts for the fact that all the blood appeared to be in the lungs, with little in the general circulation. So we can conclude that William died from the complications of a fractured clavicle; he developed pneumonia, which complicated his pre-existing heart trouble, and probably suffered a terminal pulmonary embolism.

His funeral was a very quiet affair. He was buried on Sunday 12 April in private at midnight. Mary had received a most regal funeral, but William's was hardly noticed. As usual, a wax effigy was made to be carried on his funeral chariot, which went through the streets at the dead of night. The service in Westminster Abbey was brief and as the King was placed in his vault, the officers of the King's household broke their staffs and threw them into the vault, shouting, 'Long live Queen Anne!' William, the 'stranger' King, had reached his last resting-place.

Anne

∼

Born 1 February 1665
Died Kensington, 1 August 1714

A NNE WAS the second daughter of James II and his wife Anne Hyde. The child by her mother's first pregnancy did not live and her second child was a daughter, Mary. A boy, James, Duke of Cambridge, followed and then came Anne in 1665. A second brother was born in 1666, but he was to survive for only a few hours. At this time, Anne Hyde herself became ill, probably from carcinoma of the breast, from which she was to die in 1671. Altogether she had five pregnancies with two live children. James was to have a normal son and daughter by his second wife, Mary of Modena.

Anne was a very pleasant child, quiet in disposition. She had trouble with her eyes from a very early age, as they tended to water, and her vision was very poor, a defect which was to continue all her life. At the age of four, she was sent to France for treatment, but there was no improvement, and she was unable to read or similarly use her eyes for any length of time. Mary also had difficulty with her vision. There is an account of the two young princesses seeing an object in the park, which Mary said was a man and Anne a tree. As they came nearer, it became obvious that the figure was a man, but Anne still insisted that it was a tree.

Anne, the younger and much the more retiring, was very much the 'second sister' and it was only natural that she should turn to one of her girlfriends for support. Anne chose a somewhat older girl, Sarah Churchill, and this friendship was to persist into adult life.

At the age of 15, Anne married George of Denmark. He was a

man of 30, a soldier who was much addicted to the bottle and his food. His ability did not impress either Charles II or James II and William, at a later date, snubbed every effort he made to take military command. There is no doubt, however, that Anne came to love him sincerely and they were to comfort one another in the many trials they were to undergo. Anne's marriage took place on 28 July 1683 and from this date until 1710, Anne had no fewer than 17 pregnancies, with repeated miscarriages.

Her obstetric history deserves closer study. Her first pregnancy resulted in a daughter, who was stillborn. Anne obviously became pregnant with no difficulty and she had two more daughters in 1685 and 1686, but unfortunately both children died of smallpox. Three further miscarriages followed in quick succession and then a boy was born in 1689, William, Duke of Gloucester. After Gloucester there followed two more children, a boy and a girl, but they both died in less than a day. Following this she had no fewer than eight further pregnancies which produced no living child, one of them being a twin pregnancy.

It is also known that when she was 33, Anne developed polyarthritis. This meant that she had attacks of arthritis affecting several joints in a migratory fashion. Her feet, knees, hands and other joints were all affected and the condition was very painful. At the same time, she became very obese, to such a degree that she had to be carried to her coronation. She also developed a skin condition, which caused her great concern, as both she and her sister Mary had been renowned for their beautiful fair skin. The obesity was associated with 'dropsy and gout in the bowels'.

Today, we can understand such a medical history much better. In 1975, the medical press reported the finding of an antibody in the blood of certain women. Described as an antithromboplastin, it causes a series of miscarriages. These might precede a number of other symptoms, including arthritis in many joints, facial skin eruptions and blotching. Kidney damage may also occur with water retention, dropsy and obesity. The condition has come to be known as lupus erythematosus and it is very likely that this was the cause of Anne's troubles. Other causes, syphilis and porphyria, have been suggested, but there is little to support either possibility.

Anne's one son lived for 11 years, and was given the title of Duke of Gloucester. It was obvious from an early age that he was not strong: he had a swelling on the back of his head which varied in size and is not accurately described, and it was apparently very difficult to get him to suckle until a certain Mrs Peck, who was far from clean, was used as a wet nurse. He took her milk immediately and was happy to feed. Gloucester passed through his infancy with several 'attacks', or 'fits' as they are described. The swelling on his head slowly enlarged and the physicians treated this by repeated aspiration of fluid. A defect of the head can produce a swelling in which the fluid surrounding the brain escapes, giving rise to a soft mass which is most commonly found at the back of the head where it joins the neck. Aspiration of the fluid can help, but there is a considerable risk of introducing infection; this has dangerous consequences, since the infection can easily pass to the meninges covering the brain, giving rise to meningitis. However, little Gloucester was fortunate and continued to be an active little boy, playing at soldiers, and even having a small army of children to obey his commands. Anne was a very loving and caring mother and it is obvious that they developed a great mutual regard.

At the age of nine, Gloucester was given his own household and Marlborough was appointed as his governor. He continued to prosper until his eleventh birthday in July 1700. The day after this celebration, he fell ill with a sore throat, fever and nausea. He was treated by the doctors in attendance, who immediately bled him. As he did not improve, they sent for the eminent Dr Radcliffe, who, on being told of the bleeding, said: 'Then you have destroyed him and you may finish him for I will not prescribe.' Presumably he saw that treatment was of no avail and he did not wish to be associated with the outcome. The young boy lived for a further five days in constant delirium, while Anne sat with him and prayed. When he died, Anne was stunned with grief, unable to weep, and maintaining a great composure. His death must have been the worst blow in her life, which was so full of unhappy events.

As time passed, Anne suffered still further from lupus erythematosus, possibly associated with renal failure, so that she became grossly obese. Her husband also became very fat, to such a degree that in later life the couple were incapable of sexual intercourse. George also suffered many attacks of illness which confined him to his bed, but he had an ever-faithful nurse in his wife, who would sit with him for hours holding hands.

When Mary died without issue, Anne became a much more important figure and William became reconciled to her, even starting to be polite to George. He was however, unable to hide his contempt for his stout middle-aged sister-in-law and her overweight and somewhat ridiculous husband. Anne was granted a suitable income by Parliament and lived in reasonable luxury until 1702, when William finally died. Her coronation took place in spite of her suffering from severe swelling of her legs, so severe that she was to achieve the distinction of being the only monarch to be carried to Westminster Abbey for the ceremony. Her continued ill health was, however, tempered by a high sense of duty.

Thus the short-sighted little girl became Queen. She was a very popular Queen, who was much more in tune with her people than William and Mary had been, and the first years of her reign were a great success. She naturally wanted to make her dear George leader of her armies. Under John Churchill, who was created Duke of Marlborough, there were numerous victories over the French in the next few years, a period of unparalleled military success. Anne was able to perform her duties as queen well enough; she did not try to read material, but had all matters explained to her by ministers. In spite of her poor health she opened Parliament, attended at the House of Lords and took an active part in the constant struggle of Tories versus Whigs. She was supported by her friendship with Sarah Churchill, Duchess of Marlborough, and the story of their friendship has been detailed many times. Their final quarrel must have been a sad event in the life of a woman who had few remaining friends.

Anne was by now becoming addicted to alcohol and excessive quantities of food. She suffered from gross obesity and gout, with recurrent swelling of the left leg. It was obvious that she would bear no live children and in 1701, Parliament passed the Act of Settlement by which the Crown passed to the Hanoverian line. Anne received a letter from her brother, who was exiled in France, asking her to recognise the Stuart claims to the throne, but she did not reply. This is particularly interesting because she had never liked the Hanoverians; when she was young, George of Hanover had come to England to meet her to consider the possibility of marriage. She took an instant dislike to him and this had persisted ever since, which makes it somewhat strange that she did not now support the Stuart claim. However, the Act of Settlement passed the throne to her cousin Sophie, and after her to Sophie's son, George.

In the winter of 1708–9, Anne's husband George became ill and in spite of her loving attention he died. She was now a lonely 'old' woman, although she was only 43. Many of her friends and her sister, father and husband were all dead. She came to rely particularly on her chief physician, Sir George Hamilton, but it was obvious that she was becoming infirm and possibly mentally incapable.

Anne's condition of lupus erythematosus, combined with her numerous pregnancies, must have produced a condition of anaemia coupled with renal and possibly hepatic damage. Gout and alcoholism combined to make her confused and this was compounded by her progressively bad sight. By 1713, her difficulty in walking had become more marked and by July of that year, she could not walk at all. In December she became seriously ill with fever and suffered a partial loss of consciousness which lasted for several hours. From this time on, she remained confused. Her appearance altered so much that after her illness, whenever she appeared, she was always heavily made up.

The following March, her cousin, Sophie, who would have become Queen if she had outlived Anne, died. Thus Sophie's son, George, became heir to the throne. Anne decided to send her friend Sir George Hamilton to Hanover to acquaint them with the state of affairs. On 28 July she attended the council, but was ill on the following day with sleeplessness, confusion and a nosebleed. She was cupped and bled and had no fewer than seven doctors in attendance who, as was often the case at that time, did everything most unlikely to give improvement. She was bled again, which must have made her severely anaemic; hot irons were used to blister her skin; cardis was given to make her vomit; her feet were covered with garlic; her head was shaved of her very fine hair. But the poor woman struggled on until Sunday 1 August, when she died. 'Sleep was never more welcome to a very weary traveller than death was to her.'

In his *Memories of the Court of England 1668–1706*, Jessop writes:

> On Wednesday December 23rd, her Majesty was uneasy all night with the gout of her foot. The next morning it went entirely off and she said that she was well, but about one o'clock the next day

her Majesty complained of pain in her thigh; was seized with a violent rigor and horror which lasted two hours. Extreme heat followed, with intense thirst, great anxiety, restlessness and in quietude. The pulse was planus, durus, jerrarilis et frequens which symptoms I found next day at my arrival upon which I was very much pressed bleeding, but it was not agreed to; and these symptoms continued in some measure until four o'clock on Saturday morning, at which time her Majesty fell asleep, and waked refreshed, and the next morning there was a perfect intermission of symptoms but the pulse in my opinion was not quiet. The next night, about twelve, she was attacked with an exacerbation of the fever which lasted all day and I believe till midnight if not all that night; for I was of the opinion the pulse was not quite the next day, though all the other symptoms of exacerbation went off. No exacerbation appeared after this, but I all along declared that I did not like the pulse; there was no perfect intermission of the fever, but that the pulse was at work to separate the morbific matter into the gout or some worse shape. The pain in the thigh increased until three or four doses of the bark were given, and I laid a stress upon having that part examined, but it was called a fit of the gout though I answered that it could not properly be so called in the muscles. I take this to be an inflammatory fever from a translation of the gout, and not a common ague or intermittent ague; that after nearly thirty-nine hours continuance there was a perfect remission but not intermission.

On Thursday March 11th the 'person' was seized with chilliness, vomiting and pain in the leg, the pulse was disordered and in a manner two months ago, except that the 'person' did not shiver but the chilliness and the cold continued twelve hours, and was then succeeded by a very great heat, thirst and all the symptoms of high fever which lasted till the next evening. On Sunday things were so well that a chicken was eaten with great appetite.

May 26th. The St Anthony's Fire, which broke out in her leg and thigh has considerably diminished the violence of her fever but it is believed that on the other hand that a mortification may follow. She sleeps little and eats nothing.

The disorder under which the Queen laboured at length subsided into a state of lethargic unconsciousness in which she continued for several days before she died on the morning of the 1st of August 1714.'

Guy's Hospital Gazette of 1910 gives us some detail of the post-mortem findings. As the writer explains, the post-mortem is not an examination as such, but merely the findings made while the body is being prepared for embalming:

> Upon opening the body of her late Majesty of blessed memory we found a small umbilical hernia omentalis without any excoriation, a large omentum well coloured, no water in the cavity of the abdomen. The stomach thin and its inner coat too smooth. The liver not schireous but very tender and flaccid as were all the rest of the viscera of the lower belly. The gall bladder, kidneys and urinary bladder without any stone. There was a very small scorbutic ulcer on the left leg. We can give no further account being forbid making any other inspection than was absolutely for embalming the body.

We are now able to read these reports with greater understanding. Queen Anne was indeed a very unfortunate person. She had been an attractive and happy young girl, liked by all and with a great wish to love and to be loved. She showed great affection for her husband and they both must have suffered terribly from the ease with which she became pregnant, only to lose child after child. That she had an antibody in her blood was, of course, completely unknown at the time, and the fact that they did not know the cause for her suffering must have been a great trial. The way she loved and cherished her only live child, a deformed little boy, shines through history to her great credit. The fortitude with which she accepted his early death gives an insight into her strong character.

The attractive young girl changed in early adult life into a grossly overweight woman with multiple joint pains and an inability to walk. Her sight remained very poor, a condition for which she compensated by having all material read to her. Her fine complexion became blotched and coarsened so that she had to wear heavy make-up. Child after child died at birth and their little bodies were wrapped and placed in the tomb of Mary, Queen of Scots in Westminster Abbey. (Why they should be placed with Mary we will never know.) Finally, her beloved husband died and she was alone without children or support. Her terrible affliction of lupus erythematosus continued with kidney failure, gross obesity and severe multiple joint pains. Her medical attendants gave her further suffering by their useless methods of treatment and finally the poor woman died. As a royal invalid she displayed a fortitude and a courage that are admirable.

George I

~

Born 28 May 1660
Died Osnabrück, 21 June 1727

B Y T H E A C T O F S E T T L E M E N T , the Elector of Hanover
inherited the British throne to become George I. When Queen
Anne died, he was 54 and had grown into an unattractive, middle-
aged man. He remained essentially Hanoverian and was never to
learn, or to try to learn, English. His marriage to Sophia Dorothea
of Celle, by whom he had two children, had lasted some 12 years
from 1682. George also had his mistresses and his marriage was not
free from trouble. In 1689, a Count Philip von Koenigsmark was
appointed as a colonel of dragoons at court; he was a soldier of fortune and in many ways attractive. He courted the rather stupid
Sophia Dorothea, who, being bored and flattered by his attention,
returned his advances. How far their friendship developed is not
known, but they both failed to take notice of warnings, and by 1694
Koenigsmark's boasting endangered the family honour. Eventually
he was murdered and action was taken against Sophia Dorothea,
who was imprisoned in the castle of Ahlden, where she remained
for some 30 years. George acted with particular malice towards her
and it is possible that his attitude to her was the start of the prolonged and bitter hatred between him and their son, the Prince of
Wales.

When Queen Anne died on 1 August 1714, George was immediately notified. A request was sent that he should come at once to
England, but he was in no hurry to leave his native land and did not
arrive in England until 6 September. He came with a large
entourage, including one of his two mistresses, a certain Sophia

von Kielmansegge, who was to become the Countess of Darlington. His 'senior' mistress, Mademoiselle Schulenberg, was to follow later; she was to become the Duchess of Kendal and it was with her that George was to spend so much of his time. As he never learnt the manners or the language of his kingdom, he could not participate in English social life, nor did he attempt to have a court with the usual court life. Neither of the two mistresses were attractive and were described as 'ugly old trolls', and given the nicknames 'the Maypole and the Elephant'. This somewhat unattractive man, with his two unattractive mistresses, left affairs of state to be attended to by his ministers, but the vanity and greed of the Hanoverians spread bribery and corruption until it became a feature of eighteenth-century political life.

The Jacobites made a half-hearted attempt to reinstate James Stuart in 1715, but the Old Pretender, as he was known, was never a person likely to regain a throne.

George visited his beloved Hanover as often as he was able. On his visits he frequently went to Bad Pyrmont to take the waters and the 'cure'. On 9 October 1723, while on a visit to Charlottenburg, he had a 'fainting attack', which was quite severe and may well have been a minor stroke. He recovered, but by 1724–5 he was finding that travel was very 'tiring'. One thing he did towards the end of his reign which pleased his British subjects was to take an English mistress, Ann Brett. She was the daughter of the Countess of Macclesfield, a very dark woman with black hair, a dark complexion and a Spanish appearance. His new mistress set to work to see if she could supplant the previous two, but did not manage to get complete dominance.

Throughout his reign, George quarrelled with his son, the Prince of Wales, and from time to time the quarrels became very intense. The hatred of the Georges for their sons was to become a feature of their reigns. When George I went abroad it was difficult to establish any satisfactory style of government. However, he continued with his wish to return 'home' and he decided to make a visit in the summer of 1727.

The King left St James's at the early hour of seven o'clock on 14 June for Osnabrück, where he was to meet his various relatives. He arrived at Greenwich, where he boarded his yacht. Accustomed to these travels, he was accompanied by a small band of supporters, while other members of his party followed in various boats and yachts. George sailed without delay, but was then held up by contrary winds and by the heavy weather, being able to cross only on 16 June, when he made a quick crossing. He was transferred to a Dutch yacht which was sent out to meet him by the States General (the Dutch government), which landed at Schoonhoven in the evening of 18 June. So far he had been in reasonable health on the journey. At Schoonhoven a carriage awaited him, but his baggage, including his bed, went on ahead. Travelling with him in his carriage were Hardenberg, his court marshal and Fabrice, his Hanoverian *Kammerherr*. He was guarded by a detachment of Dutch cavalry and his body servants followed behind. The other court officials, male and female, Hanoverian and British, made their way in a variety of carriages. The picture we get of the journey is one of orderly confusion, with George most anxious to hurry ahead.

On 18 June at ten o'clock at night he halted at a place called Varth, where he dined. His party had not been expected and no special arrangements were made for him; the meal was very poor by his standards. Nevertheless, George was up at five o'clock the following morning, anxious to push ahead. On this day he stopped at Apeldoorn at midday to have a meal, an unusual occurrence and possibly due to the fact that the meal the previous evening had been so inadequate. Certainly, Fabrice reported that this was the first time he had so stopped in all the many journeys they had made together.

Here it is that tradition plays a role. It is said that in the illness prior to her death, Sophia Dorothea wrote a letter to her husband declaring herself innocent of the charges made against her and accusing him of cruelty and injustice. Moreover, she summoned him to meet her within a year and a day before the tribunal of God. She gave the letter to a friend to be delivered to the King by hand, but it had been some seven months before the visit to the continent made delivery possible. It is reported that the letter was passed to the King as he sat in his coach, on the evening of the 19th, at Delden. He then had supper and spent the evening in conversation with some Dutch people who had asked for an audience. It has been said that the letter caused the King to become very upset and precipitated events. However, George was a very unemotional individual and seems unlikely that he would be upset by a letter.

The next day the party set out at seven o'clock. George, Hardenberg and Fabrice travelled with their Dutch guard. The King announced that he had passed a bad night with stomach pains, probably from eating oranges and strawberries at supper. The courtiers suggested a halt to give him time to recover, but George wanted to push on. After half an hour, he stopped the carriage to attend to a call of nature. When he returned, Hardenberg noted that his face was distorted and that he was having difficulty in moving his right hand. Fabrice asked for permission to attend to his hand. George then became pale and either fainted or became unconscious. There was a surgeon in a following coach, since both Fabrice and Hardenberg had been unwell; never before on the King's travels had one been so near at hand. While Hardenberg went to fetch the surgeon, Fabrice placed smelling salts under the King's nose.

On seeing the King, the surgeon at once diagnosed a stroke and advised that the King be bled immediately. The King was taken out of the coach and laid on the grass, where he was bled by the surgeon, only a few minutes after he had suffered his attack. As he was being lifted back into the coach, he recovered consciousness and indicated with his left hand that he wanted to continue. The party went slowly on and for the next half-hour the King was lucid and could say a few words. He then fell into a 'sleep' which appeared to be quite unnatural, with very deep snoring. A Dutch officer was sent ahead to see if he could locate the King's bed, and a message was sent back to the King's physician Steigerdahl, who was far back in the cavalcade.

George appeared to be getting worse. He was held in the arms of the three attendants, Fabrice, Hardenberg and the surgeon, while they again considered what might be done. The King was placed once more on the ground and plasters were applied to his hand and neck and strong spirits were given, but all to no effect. Messages were sent to Lingen to fetch the physicians of Friedrich Wilhelm, but both these were away. Hardenberg decided to continue to Osnabrück, as he was assured by the surgeon that the movements of the coach would in no way damage the King. Messages were sent ahead, and those who waited to welcome the King were told to disperse. The King was carried along secret stairs into his room to avoid publicity. He arrived at Osnabrück between 10 and 11 o'clock. Blood was again let during the night of 20–21 June, with no effect. His state of unconsciousness persisted and at about half an hour after midnight the King died. It seems certain that George had suffered a cerebral haemorrhage or a cerebral thrombosis, causing a stroke. No autopsy was performed, since he had instructed that his body was not to be opened or embalmed.

England waited for the return of the King's body, but it became plain that he was to remain in Hanover. George II decided that his father should be buried in Hanover in the Leineschloss Church. The church was severely damaged during World War II, and when rebuilding took place the King's sarcophagus and that of his mother were moved to the nineteenth-century mausoleum in the Herrenhausen Garden. It is here that it now resides.

George II

~

Born 10 November 1683
Died Westminster, 12 October 1760

WHEN GEORGE I came to England in 1714 in accordance with the Act of Settlement, he was accompanied by his son, George Augustus, who was 31 at the time, and had been married for nine years. The man who was to become George II was a dapper little figure who carried himself in a very erect manner; he was well built with prominent blue eyes, a masterful nose and jaw, and a ruddy complexion. As a boy, he sided with his mother, Sophia Dorothea, and was very distressed when she was incarcerated in the Castle of Ahlden. Indeed, one of the first things he did on becoming King was to prominently display a portrait of her; although his mother had been indiscreet, George retained very fond memories. An antagonism developed between the young prince and his father which became a real hatred by the time they reached England.

George Augustus received the usual training of a German prince, but, unlike his father, could also speak French, Italian and English. His intellectual interests were somewhat limited and his conversation consisted of military matters, pleasantries and badinage. He spoke in a loud voice, with a marked accent. He distinguished himself at the Battle of Oudenarde, where he behaved with great courage, subsequently developing visions of himself as a great military commander.

He married Caroline of Ansbach, with whom he seemed to be genuinely in love. Before proposing marriage, he visited Ansbach incognito, and he was charmed with what he saw. They were married in 1705, but it was 17 months before they had a child, a son. Although the boy was to be in direct line of succession to the throne of England, there were no official witnesses to the birth and little or no celebrations followed. His father referred to him as Wechselbalg, which means changeling, or the 'Griffe', which is a term for a half-caste. He grew up as 'Poor Fred', with a Semitic nose and a very sallow complexion. There are various theories to explain why he should have been so disliked by his parents. One is that he was a child smuggled into the palace to replace the stillborn child of Caroline (in the same way as the child of James II was supposed to have been brought in, in a bedpan). This is most improbable, as is the theory that the child was a bastard, as George and Caroline were still very much in love at the time of his birth. The matter remains a mystery. Prince Frederick was to die before his father, but not before he had sired the future George III.

During 1716, the relationship between George Augustus and his father became even worse, until Augustus, now Prince of Wales, established his own court. In 1716 George Augustus and Caroline had the misfortune to have a stillborn prince. In November 1717 they had another son, but his christening brought new friction, so severe that George I put his son under house arrest. Reconciliation was prolonged and never complete.

Just as George Augustus's relationship with his father had been one of continued animosity, so his relationship with his son Frederick also deteriorated. As Prince of Wales after his father's accession, Frederick complained that he had nothing interesting to do, but he was still offered no occupation by his father. He was a keen gambler, despite being kept short of money by his parents. He amused himself with conversation, music, gaming and cricket, and had a barge which could out-row the King's. He had a number of mistresses and illegitimate children, but was in poor health from a gall bladder disease which gave him recurrent attacks of severe pain.

In 1735, George II visited Hanover and while there fell in love with Amelia Sophia von Walmoden, a courtesan. He acquired her for the sum of 1,000 ducats, which was said to be a tribute more to his economy than to his ardour. Indeed, he consulted his wife by letter in the negotiation for her, and still displayed his love for Caroline. At this time, he had been suffering from attacks of piles, a complaint which he tried to keep private. He developed a fistula, an infected track from the rectum to the buttock. This is a very painful and distressing complaint and difficult to cure. He underwent an operation which afforded some improvement.

In 1736, the King again visited his mistress in Hanover. The meeting was somewhat marred when he found a ladder from her bedroom and a young officer hiding in the garden. The King again consulted his wife and ministers and he was advised to leave matters as they were and neglect her shortcomings. However, a foreign mistress made him far from popular, particularly because there was no doubt that she was very expensive. He stayed too long in Hanover, which increased his unpopularity, so he returned to London, where, in 1737, he had a severe attack of piles.

On 9 November 1737 Queen Caroline fell ill with what was described as severe colic. She had in fact developed an intestinal obstruction caused by a strangulated umbilical hernia. An umbilical hernia is due to the profusion of the bowel through a weak navel. There is no real danger if the small sac which forms has a wide entrance, since the bowel suffers no danger. However, if the entrance is very narrow, the bowel may suffer from compression with damage to its blood supply. In this case the condition is described as being strangulated and there is danger that the bowel may necrose and cause peritonitis. The passage of material along the bowel is also prevented, leading to colic and obstruction. This is what was now happening to the queen, who had been very anxious to hide the fact that she had a hernia and had told no doctor of its presence.

Doctors at the time did not examine royalty but merely prescribed. They tried cordial, mint-water, brandy and elixir, all to no avail. She was also bled. Two more physicians were called in and more remedies given; purges, blisters and glisters (or irritants) were applied. It was not until 11 November that the King insisted on telling the surgeon, Ranby, what was really the matter. The queen still tried to hide the hernia, but Ranby found it and told her that he must operate. Three surgeons now attended and argued about the procedure. The correct operation would have been to enlarge the hole through which the hernia protruded, to relieve the pressure on the bowel and the obstruction. They decided instead to lance the swelling, letting out much offensive matter, but in no way altering the final outcome. It is possible that they did not perform the correct operation, since it carried the risk of failure: at this time operative treatment had a mortality of some 80 per cent. Perhaps the surgeons chose the simple operation of lancing because it would offer slight improvement without the danger of her dying immediately afterwards and bringing blame upon themselves. Gangrene now set in, affecting the tissues surrounding the umbilicus. Caroline was a very long-suffering person who did not complain throughout her ordeal. She now expressed her last wish, that her husband should remarry.

In spite of her critical condition, her son was not allowed to come to see her. Initially, the gangrene did not spread and her condition seemed to improve somewhat, leading the doctors to suggest that there was a faint hope of recovery. However, on the 17th, her condition became much worse with a further rupture of bowel. She required several further incisions, bearing all with great fortitude. She was even able to show her sense of humour, asking Ranby if he would not like to do all this probing and cutting to his wife, whom he was said to dislike. The King, meanwhile, stayed with her, making fatuous remarks which included asking why she should vomit so: 'My God, if you do not like a thing why call for it?' The queen bore all her troubles well, even the tiresome King. On the 20th, she asked how long she was likely to last and took leave of the King, thanking him for all his goodness. She was by now very dehydrated and toxic and suffering some confusion, but she was able to say at the last, 'I believe I have now got an asthma … open the window … pray.' The King's grief was tender and unaffected.

The King now sent for Amelia Sophia von Walmoden as a consolation, and his violent dislike for his son Frederick somewhat abated. George was to reign for 23 years after the death of his wife. He had the war with Spain and the Jacobite revolution of 1745 to occupy him. Every other year he still visited Hanover. In 1751, Frederick, Prince of Wales, died. The new Prince of Wales cost some £30,000 a year less than his father, a fact that greatly pleased George. By 1755, George thought that it was time his grandson married and he selected a suitable bride, Princess Sophia of Brunswick-Wolfenbuttel, a girl of 17 and not unattractive. However, the Princess Dowager turned her son against the match. The prince having failed in duty and obedience to his grandfather, the old state of family hatred was renewed. Frederick later married Augusta of Saxe-Gotha.

Death was to come to George II on 12 October 1760. As there had been throughout so much of his life, an element of farce existed then. He rose at six in the morning, as he was accustomed, drank his chocolate and went to his close-stool. His valet de chambre heard 'a noise louder than the royal wind' accompanied by a groan, and went into the chamber. There he found that the King had fallen and cut his face on a piece of furniture. He was taken to his bed and doctors were urgently called. They tried to bleed him at once, but not a drop of blood would flow. It was thus obvious that he had died – nothing could be done to help. One of the ventricles of his heart had ruptured, forcing the blood out into the pericardium, which surrounds the heart. This blood immediately constricted the other ventricle, causing a complete loss of blood to the brain with a terminal loss of consciousness.

In his *History of George II*, Walpole writes:

> On October 25th, he rose as usual at six, and drank his chocolate. A quarter after seven he went into the little closet. His German valet de chambre in waiting heard a noise and running in found the king lying dead on the floor. In falling he had cut his face on the corner of the bureau. He was lain on the bed and blooded, but not a drop followed; the ventricle of his heart had burst.

In the *Transactions of the Royal Society 1761*, Francis Nicholis writes:

> Post mortem report; On opening the abdomen, all the parts therein contained were found in a natural and healthy state, except that some hydatids, or watery bladders, were found between the substance of each kidney and its internal coat. None of them exceeded the bulk of a common walnut. The brain was found in a healthy state, noways loaded with blood.
>
> The lungs were in a natural state, free from every appearance of inflammation or tubercle, but upon examining the heart, its pericardium was found distended with a quantity of blood nearly sufficient to fill a pint cup, and upon removing this blood a round orifice appeared in the middle of the upper side of the right ventricle of the heart, large enough to admit the extremity of the little finger. Through this orifice, all the blood brought to the right

ventricle had been discharged into the cavity of the pericardium. The auricles and ventricles were found absolutely void of blood, either in a fluid or congealed state. The two great arteries of the right ventricle were stretched beyond their natural state and in the trunk of the aorta, we found a transverse fissure on its inner side about an inch and a half long, through which some blood had recently passed under its external coat and formed an elevated ecchymosis. This appearance showed the true state of an incipient aneurysm of the aorta.

George II had thus died from a ruptured ventricle of the heart consequent upon aortitis, possibly syphilitic. Aneurysms of the aorta and rupture of a ventricle (heart) are commonly syphilitic in origin.

George III

~

Born 4 June 1738
Died 29 January 1820

GEORGE III was the grandson of George II. He died when he was 82, which was a great age for the times. He lived longer than any other king of England and he ruled for a longer period than any other king. He had a very pleasant and enjoyable early life and was much more stable than his two Hanoverian predecessors. He was a likeable man of simple tastes and it is tragic to witness the progressive deterioration in his mental health. This deterioration was not fully understood at the time, as was the case with almost all mental illnesses.

Naturally, George's disability was suppressed so that he might continue as king, but in time it became so marked that drastic steps had to be taken to help him. These involved severe restraint and were possibly cruel and of no help, but they may be excused given the state of medical understanding at the time. Viewing his complaint in the light of more modern thinking suggests that he may well have suffered from porphyria, a rare metabolic disorder which leads to mental and other changes.

Writings at the time of his death show how confused people were about his condition. *The Observer* of 6 February 1820 reports:

These months since a gradual loss of strength and flesh were perceptible. A slight bowel attack about six weeks ago gave considerable alarm and though it lasted but two days, it left his Majesty much debilitated. No actual bodily malady existed from that time until the early part of last week when a renewal of the bowel complaint showed that the bodily functions had lost their power. Everything that he took passed through him as he received it.

The Times of 31 January 1820 writes:

> In November 1819 he suffered from a severe cold and later from a species of diarrhoea, which after some days yielded to anodyne and astringent medicines. After January 6th the diarrhoea returned with greater violence and made visible inroads on his strength. He suffered much from chilliness, although the temperature of the room was kept high. It was not until two days of his death that he kept his bed entirely; although before this he had risen later than was his custom. In the morning of January 29th he became much weaker and at 8.35 p.m. he died without a struggle or apparently having any pain. His sanity did not return in his last hours.

At long last George III had come to the end of his suffering. It is only in very recent times that a medical appreciation of his physical condition has provided any clue as to what affected him. There is no doubt that George III died in terminal dementia. He had been blind and deaf for several years and was receiving 'treatment' for his continued insanity. The point of interest is to consider how he reached this state and whether his mental state was an idiopathic insanity or the result of some physical infirmity causing temporary and recurrent mental aberration.

His reign was a remarkable period. The ascendancy of Parliament over the monarchy had been firmly established. The country was threatened by Napoleon, but saved by Nelson and Wellington. The American colonies were lost, but of even greater import was this: when George became King, Britain ruled a few scattered islands, whereas at the end of his reign she ruled a territory unequalled in the history of nations. What, then, was the state of the King who had reigned during this time?

As a young man George III led a very healthy life. He was fond of physical exercise and he ate with moderation, which was a very unusual attribute at that time. He was indeed moderate in all things and a very faithful husband. In youth he had a pleasant disposition, taking an interest in many matters, including science, of which he showed considerable knowledge. His beautiful microscope is still preserved in an Oxford college.

It was in June 1788 that the first evidence of the trouble that was to follow became evident. The King was seized with a bilious fever attended with violent spasms in his stomach and bowels; his diarrhoea lasted some days. He himself wrote to Pitt the Younger to say that he had had 'a pretty smart bilious attack'. His continued illness is well documented and it is obvious from several sources that the condition was essentially a physical one, with biliousness followed by considerable prostration and a somewhat prolonged convalescence. George was at Cheltenham at the time, and this attack is called the Cheltenham episode. He seemed to recover completely. At this time he was at the height of his popularity; his simple manner and the way he mixed with the crowd in Cheltenham earned him widespread acclaim, making him a contrast to the previous two kings.

In August of that year he had an 'influenzal attack'. Then on Friday 17 October 1788 George was again seized with acute abdominal pain together with pain in his legs. The pain lasted all day and was of considerable intensity, in spite of the laudanum which was administered. He also had a red rash and his physician noted 'some yellowness in the eyes and urine bilious', which meant it was dark in colour. The medical men who attended the King did so with strict attention to decorum. They did not examine the patient, but limited their observations to taking his pulse and regarding his 'animal functions'. Nor did they speak unless first addressed by the King. We thus do not have any real clinical picture of the King's state. The condition recurred and by the end of October he was described as being in a state of delirium, suffering from several attacks of agitation along with an inability to write clearly or attend to affairs of state. Mental impairment was now accompanying the physical attacks: not only was George's memory affected, but he also had difficulty with his vision and his hearing was impaired too. It seems to be a sad fact that the King realised he was losing control of his body and mind before this became evident to his medical attendants. The doctors ascribed his trouble to such trivialities as 'having not taken off his wet stockings, but keeping them on'; the possibility of gout was also considered. It is plain that his doctors did not know what to do and that they had no real understanding of the nature of his complaint.

The King was now troubled by weakness in the legs and the

arms, hoarseness, an inability to focus his vision, and difficulty in concentration, followed by mounting excitement and sleeplessness. These attacks left the King greatly weakened. By November, his condition had become so severe that he was said to be in constant 'delirium'. The physical condition seemed to improve, but the mental state did not. George was moved to Kew, with considerable difficulty as he did not wish to leave Windsor, and there he was 'restrained' with a jacket on several occasions.

At Kew his physicians enlisted the help of the Willis family, medical men who specialised in mental derangement. They took over control of the King and often restrained him. He had many other medical treatments, including repeated treatment with tartar emetic. Eventually, and with setbacks, the King started to improve in spite of his treatment. By the end of February, he was almost completely recovered and the Regency Bill, by which power would have passed to his son, had not yet reached its third reading. In March he had recovered so far that many of his attendants were dismissed, although the King was said to be very thin and his voice very weak. He decided to convalesce at Weymouth and here he bathed in the sea and took increased exercise. His health continued to improve and he was now to enjoy some 12 years of good health, interrupted only by some minor episodes. He displayed mild symptoms, being sensitive to sunlight and finding the heat of the sun oppressive. He also suffered minor attacks of abdominal pain, especially in 1795.

A considerable number of physicians speculated with regard to the illness, and never before was psychiatric medicine so much discussed. Indeed, the King's illness did much for psychiatric patients and their treatment. 'Small wonder that his debilitated state of the body had been made worse by being bled, blistered, vomited and purged while simultaneously being deprived of usual comforts and consolations.' Most now labelled his illness 'a feverish symptomatic delirium'.

In the second week of February 1801, George suffered a second major attack of his illness. He was very bilious at the onset and the condition turned out to repeat, on a smaller scale, his trouble in the period 1788–89. His physical symptoms were colic, constipation, hoarseness, muscular pains and weakness, sweating, a fast pulse and sleeplessness, leading to delirium and coma. It was also stated that his urine was dark. The attack was ascribed to his catching cold while at church on 13 February. It lasted until June, when the King went once again to Weymouth for a period of convalescence. By August he was once more in reasonable health.

For three years he continued in reasonable health and then in February 1804 there was another recurrence. Once again the illness took the form it had on previous occasions, with the usual physical signs and symptoms followed by mental disturbance. After a period of some four months, George once again went to Weymouth, still suffering from severe headaches. His improvement on this occasion was slow and there was mild recurrent trouble. In 1805 he suffered from a progressive deterioration in his sight. The right eye became almost totally blind and the left eye deficient. It was stated that his trouble came from cataracts. He required a reader, although he persisted with efforts to conduct his own affairs. By September 1805 he was to all intents and purposes blind. With intermittent attacks and various treatments, the King slowly deteriorated and the Regency had to be established in 1811, lasting until his death in 1820.

The details of his progressive decline are recorded in great detail and as his state altered, so were the various affairs of state affected. The Prince of Wales acted almost continuously as regent, while the King continued with varying treatments, slowly becoming weaker, deafer and more senile. By 1817 he was totally deaf and his contact with the outside world became almost completely cut off. He continued with mixed physical and mental trouble until late in December 1819, when he had his last paroxysm. This was severe and he sank progressively, finally dying at eight o'clock on 20 January 1820.

It has recently been shown that there is a group of inherited metabolic defects which lead to an alteration in the blood chemistry as toxic substances accumulate, damaging the nervous system. A rare variety is called porphyria, a reference to the fact that the urine is found to be purple, or dark in colour, either on passing or after it has been left to stand. This biochemical abnormality is due to a disturbance of porphyrin metabolism. The number of purple-red pigments in the body markedly increases, so that their excess in the blood causes widespread intoxication of the nervous system. They appear in the urine and today can be easily recognised. The damage they cause to the central nervous system results in painful weakness and possibly an over-sensitivity of some parts. When the autonomic nerves are affected, these in turn have an impact on the heart, gastro-intestinal system and sweat glands, and lead to nausea, colic, constipation, rapid pulse, agitation, excitement, overactivity, rambling, sleeplessness and confusion. All these symptoms were displayed by George in varying degrees and on various occasions, as were delirium, confusion, stupor and convulsions. The treatment he received may well have aggravated his trouble. Since he had lucid intervals when he was more or less normal, he must have been very distressed by the treatment he was given.

The cause of porphyria appearing in an individual is a hereditary factor. It may remain symptomless or dormant throughout life, or it may cause attacks of a varying degree of severity, with remissions and exacerbations. The illness of George III seems, in so many of its features, to be a classical description of the condition. The exact biochemical fault is not yet completely understood and there is no real treatment once an attack has occurred. The condition is merely treated symptomatically. Even today, many cases are not recognised for what they are, and patients are still treated for a variety of conditions, the real cause being missed.

We will, of course, never know for certain that George had porphyria, but a consideration of his illness offers no alternative diagnosis. From where did he inherit this disease? A full consideration of the various possibilities was published by Ida MacAlpine and Richard Hunter in their book *George III and the Mad Business*, and they suggest that the disease could be traced to James I. He had as his physician a certain Dr Myerne, who kept very extensive notes concerning his royal patient. Indeed, these records are more scientific than most of those kept in the reign of George III. They show that James I suffered from an affliction which could only be porphyria as there is a description of 'the urine being purple as Alicante Wine'.

Dr Myerne thought that James I had a renal stone and that the red coloration of his urine was due to this. Blood in the urine caused by a stone usually occurs with pain, which may be severe and aggravated by exercise. Myerne himself noted that in this case, the red colour was unusually not related to pain or to exercise.

James I also had the variant of porphyria associated with skin sensitivity. It is noted that he had a very fragile skin, which was easily injured and very sensitive to the hot summer sun. A post-mortem showed no abnormality and no evidence of any urinary stone.

James I's eldest son, Henry, died on 6 November 1612, at the age of 18, from an attack similar to those which affected his father. His death was so sudden that foul play was suspected, as it was in the case of James himself. Mary, Queen of Scots was James's mother and she seems to have suffered from porphyria, having inherited it herself from her grandmother, Margaret Tudor, the sister of Henry VIII. In all these people the same signs are to be seen, so it would appear that the Stuarts inherited the defect from the house of Tudor.

George IV

~

Born 12 August 1762
Died Windsor, 26 June 1830

WHEN THE long reign of George III finally came to an end in 1820, there were no fewer than 14 of the King's children still alive, nine sons and five daughters. His fifth son, Edward, Duke of Kent, was to die from pneumonia the same year as his father, but Edward's daughter, Victoria, was to become Queen.

George, the Prince of Wales, had a happy childhood, but as he grew up, the usual animosity which plagued the Hanoverians developed between father and son. The young prince had a series of mistresses and soon got into debt, thereby losing his father's affection. George III was a great family man who loved his wife and children, and we can well understand his annoyance that his son should behave as he did.

One of George's loves, a Mrs Fitzherbert, insisted on marriage. He did this in secret on 15 December 1785, at the age of 23, and seemed to have had a very genuine affection for her. Still, the marriage could not have been more problematic: she was a commoner; under the Royal Marriage Act of 1772, marriages were valid for royal persons under the age of 25 only with the consent of the monarch; and she was a Roman Catholic, at a time when the Act of Settlement stipulated that no person married to a Catholic could succeed to the throne. However, there is no doubt that George did love Mrs Fitzherbert, and at his death he was found to have with him a locket with her portrait. Possibly this strange marriage was to influence Edward VIII in later years.

Ten years later, George had to make a dynastic marriage. This took place on 7 April 1795, when he was married in the Chapel Royal at St James's to Princess Caroline of Brunswick. It was obvious that George had no real stomach for the matter, for he was drunk at the wedding and had to be supported. It was not a good beginning, but nevertheless, at nine months to the day, Caroline gave birth to a healthy daughter on 7 January 1796. Husband and wife never lived happily together. He had a number of mistresses, but no illegitimate children and Mrs Fitzherbert had no issue. The public sided with Caroline and their relationship added to the prince's unpopularity.

Their daughter Charlotte grew into a healthy and attractive girl who became her father's greatest delight. She married Prince Leopold of Saxe-Coburg on 2 May 1816. Given that their children would ensure the Hanoverian succession, it was with particular delight that George heard that his daughter was pregnant. During her pregnancy she had had no real difficulties and the birth was looked forward to with confidence. Dr Richard Baillie was the physician in ordinary, Sir Richard Croft was the accouchier and a Dr Simms was to be in attendance should the need for instruments arise. Unfortunately, she became unduly large in her later pregnancy, so that at one time they thought she might be having twins. The cause for her large size was probably because the foetal head had not passed down into the pelvis, as it should in the last weeks of pregnancy. Croft was the kind of doctor who demanded obedience from his patients and he put Charlotte on a reducing diet and did several bloodlettings, both of which were to her disadvantage. The first stages of delivery went well enough, but it then became obvious that there was going to be great difficulty in delivering the baby. Charlotte was in labour for no less than 52 hours. The child, a well-formed boy, was delivered dead and Charlotte was to have a post-partum delivery haemorrhage, from which she died. Sir Richard Croft was to commit suicide three months later. It is one of the most tragic of all royal births and George was naturally devastated. It was some three months before he recovered.

During George III's recurrent attacks of mental instability it had become necessary to have a regency. George IV had thus had several years of acting as head of state, before his coronation in 1820. By then, he had become very obese indeed. It was unfortunate that the fashion of the time demanded tight trousers which set off the figure of a young man, but made a fat person such as George look absurd. Cartoons of the period never fail to show his gross obesity and George himself was very conscious of his unfortunate appearance. When he was proclaimed king at Carlton House in 1820, he had been ill for some time, unable to attend at the deathbed of his father. Then, after coming from a warm room to the bitter cold of the proclamation outside Carlton House, George suffered an attack of 'pleurism', which was so bad that by 1 February he was said to be in 'imminent danger' of his life. For a while, it looked as if the longest reign of a sovereign was to be followed by the shortest, but George slowly recovered in spite of frequent bloodlettings; it is said that 150 ounces of blood were removed in all. He then went to convalesce at Brighton, where he stayed for two months.

George's coronation was disturbed by his wife attempting to enter Westminster Abbey after he had refused to have her present. George took steps to obtain a divorce, but his popularity fell, while Caroline continued to enjoy the support of the people. During the first years of his reign George IV had repeated urinary trouble which we now know was due to a diverticulum of the bladder. This, as the name implies, causes a second cavity into which urine can pass. The opening of the diverticulum into the bladder may be wide and cause little difficulty, but in George's case the opening was very narrow indeed and the urine consequently stagnated in the small cavity, becoming infected. This gave rise to repeated attacks of urinary infection, causing frequency and pain on passing water. A stone then formed in his diverticulum, which would have caused even more embarrassment in such a public figure, and this may well have contributed to his avoidance of travel in his later years. He also suffered from repeated attacks of gout. In spite of this complaint he had an excellent appetite, eating heartily and also drinking large quantities of the port wine which was so popular at the time; a glance at the menus of the many official dinners he attended explains much. Nor did he try to diet as might be expected.

It is unfortunate that throughout his life, George had few occupations to give him mental or physical stimulation. He devoted most of his attention to frivolity: dress, women, horses and gambling. From his early youth he had been able to mimic with great skill, giving excellent imitations of the various ministers, with their gestures and voices, and this he continued to do to the amusement of his friends. He did also develop quite a reasonable taste for works of art and he collected many which were to become of national importance. His interest in architecture is illustrated by the pavilion at Brighton, which he commissioned, while he was also responsible for altering Windsor Castle and involved in the rebuilding of Buckingham Palace.

In the last ten years of his life, he became progressively less and less active. He had once been able to ride very considerable distances without fatigue, but he now found travel tiring. His bladder condition must have made riding difficult. One way he tried to conserve his youth was to hold an annual ball, the Juvenile Ball, which was attended by the children of his ministers and friends. This he did right up to 1819, when he acted as an affable uncle to those present. Short of breath, he needed to sit rather than stand. He also made up his face with rouge and greasepaint and wore a wig, being aware of his own unattractive appearance. When in 1828 he asked the Duke of Wellington to form a government, he did so while propped up in bed wearing a grease-stained turban and a silk dressing gown. A somewhat pathetic figure, he even started to avoid Mrs Fitzherbert. His sight began to fail and he no doubt worried lest he should be developing his father's terminal state. Some London newspapers did not hesitate to say that he was showing some evidence of mental instability, but in this they seem to have been incorrect, and there is no evidence that he had developed porphyria. By 1829, his massive frame kept him in bed and allowed him only short periods of restricted activity. He had a series of what were described as 'minor strokes'. Numerous optimistic bulletins were issued, but George was dying of cardiorespiratory failure. We know from the post-mortem that he had a valvular disease of the heart, which would aggravate his general heart failure. His gross obesity was further complicated by gout, a bladder stone in a diverticulum and cirrhosis of the liver. This last complaint was associated with high blood pressure in his portal circulation and this finally led to a fatal gastric haemorrhage; cirrhosis is often followed by the development of varicose veins in the upper part of the stomach, and these veins are apt to rupture, giving rise to the type of bleeding which was to be the final cause of his death.

On 12 April 1830 George rode in the park for the last time. Despite no fewer than 60 bulletins being issued in an optimistic tone, he was suffering from progressive dyspnoea, or shortage of breath, along with a cough and expectoration. He also had developed marked fluid retention, or oedema, particularly in his legs. Surrounded by his attendants and clergy, we read of the end as described in *The Observer* of 28 June 1830:

> His sufferings towards the last were considerably alleviated except during the fits of coughing. On Friday night, he appeared tranquil and slept at intervals; the expectoration had ceased in the early part of the evening; about three o'clock on Saturday morning he asked to be removed from his bed to his night chair. In this position partial relief was afforded, but in a few minutes he appeared very faint, asked for sal volatile and expired almost immediately after.

A post-mortem examination was performed by Sir Astley Cooper, who had also attended on George III. *The Lancet* of 1830 states:

> The body exhibited but little sign of putrefaction and the anasarca had disappeared excepting some remains of it in the thighs. Notwithstanding the emaciation of his Majesties person, a very large amount of fat was found between the skin and the abdominal muscles. The omentum and all those parts in which fat is usually deposited were excessively loaded with it. The abdomen did not contain more than an ounce of water. The stomach and intestines were somewhat contracted; they were darker colour than natural in consequence of their containing mucous tinged with blood, and in the stomach was found a clot of pure blood weighing six ounces. The liver was pale and had an unhealthy granulated appearance. The spleen, although larger than usual, was not otherwise diseased, and the pancreas was in a sound state. The sigmoid flexure of the large intestine had formed unnatural adhesions to the bladder, accompanied by a solid inflammatory deposit of the size of an orange. Upon careful examination of this tumour, a sac or cavity was found in the centre, which contained a urinary calculus of the size of a filbert, and this cavity communicated by a small aperture with the interior of the bladder at its fundus. In other respects the bladder was healthy and the prostate gland did not appear to be enlarged. The kidneys were also free from disease. Thorax; Two pints of water were found in the cavity

of the right side and three pints and three quarters in the left side of the chest. The left lung was considerably diminished. The lower edge of each lobe of the lungs had a remarkable fringe, which upon examination was found to be formed by a deposit of fat. The substance of the lungs had undergone no change of structure, but the mucous membrane lining the air tubes was of a dark colour in consequence of its vessels being turgid with blood. The pericardium contained about half an ounce of fluid, but its opposite surface in several places adhered to each other from inflammation at some remote period. Upon the surface of the heart and pericardium there was a large amount of fat, and the muscular substance of the heart was so tender as to be lacerated by the slightest force. It was much larger than normal. Its cavities upon the right side presented no unusual appearance, but those of the left side were much dilated, more especially the auricle. The three semilunar valves at the beginning of the aorta were ossified throughout their substance and the inner coat of that blood-vessel presented an irregular surface and was in many parts ossified. The immediate cause of his Majesties' dissolution was the rupture of a blood vessel of the stomach.

George IV thus had a mixed pathology, which included gastric haemorrhage consequent upon portal hypertension, a cirrhosis of the liver, myocardial degeneration (fatty) with old pericarditis, aortic valvular disease, left ventricular hypertrophy, chronic bronchitis and fundic diverticulum of the bladder with calculus formation.

He lies buried in St George's Chapel, Windsor.

William IV

~~

Born 21 August 1765
Died Windsor, 20 June 1837

AS THE THIRD SON of the 15 children born to George III, William Henry did not appear likely to inherit the throne. His father and mother were very anxious that their children should be brought up strictly, so much so that they were never allowed to sit in the presence of their mother, making it difficult for them to dine. Although the children were all ruled with strict discipline, the eldest son proved difficult to maintain, so George III was more than anxious that his third son should not emulate his eldest brother. Sending him away to sea seemed to be a very good way of making sure that William avoided the dissolute ways of his brother and accordingly the young man was sent to sea as a midshipman. It is likely that William was not particularly intelligent; at any rate, he took to the life with great gusto. Life at sea suited him admirably and he soon became a bluff sailor, speaking his mind without restraint and using swear words in most of his conversation. He did not drink too heavily, for the times, but was very fond of hosting parties at which others were encouraged to drink to excess.

The medical history of William is therefore a naval medical history and he contracted the diseases which might be expected in a nautical man. As a child he had recurrent mild attacks of asthma, otherwise he was a reasonably fit youth. There is no doubt that he frequented brothels whilst a young man and had affairs with a variety of ladies. One strange affair concerned a certain Caroline von Linsingen, who was said to have married William at Bad Pyrmont. It is likely that the lady concerned exaggerated the affair, but there is no doubt that he had one son by a person unknown, a boy, who was brought over from Hanover by his mother and who lived in William's household. The boy served in the navy aboard the *Blenheim* and was drowned off Madagascar in 1808.

William had a number of 'friends' in Portsmouth and, like many sailors, seems to have had 'a friend in every port'. In 1787, whilst in the West Indies, he had a severe attack of fever which was associated with blotches on the skin, loss of appetite, boils and rheumatic pains. This was undoubtedly an attack of some venereal disease, most probably syphilis, for which he would have received the usual treatment including mercury and arsenic. Treatment at this time did not tend to be completely satisfactory and the disease was apt to remain in a latent form, so William may well have had a persistent syphilitic infection all his life, a condition which would account for his mental attitude in later life. However, he was to have many children and syphilis did not show in any of their histories, so the disease could not have been in a very active form.

While he was in the West Indies his affairs were recorded by a Lieutenant Dyott, who wrote: 'He would go into any house where he saw a pretty girl, and was perfectly acquainted with every house of a certain description in the town.' In the notorious 'house' of Rachel Pringle, he and his friends left damage of £700 on a wild night and the formidable lady demanded that the prince should compensate her in full. Back he came to England, and in Plymouth he fell for a Miss Winne, for whom he seems to have had a genuine affection. His father heard of the association and William was sent to Halifax. However, there he had more lady friends to compensate him, becoming involved with a Mrs Wentworth, who was one of his more mature ladies.

William was in the West Indies when he first heard of his father's illness and mental instability. He was genuinely very upset, but soon realised that under a regency he would endure fewer restrictions, since he had supported his brother in the constant struggle between father and son.

After the second attack of mental illness had struck George III, William was created Duke of Clarence. This gave him his own establishment and he now thought that he should have a more stable relationship with a possible 'wife'. He installed a Miss Polly Finch, but soon found her a 'bore', so off she went. He then started an association with a Mrs Jordan which was to last for some 20 years. She was an actress who had started, as so many had before her, by being a mistress, in her case to a certain Richard Ford, by whom she became pregnant. After she left Richard Ford she lived with a Mr Richard Daly, by whom she had two daughters. When William first began his suit she was not inclined to accept it, but as Mr Ford did not appear to offer her any permanent relationship, she responded to William. She came to live with him and from 1791, for some 20 years, they lived together in great harmony. She won approval, even from George III, who went on occasions to see her act.

William and Mrs Jordan had no fewer than ten children, four sons and six daughters. They were given the surname of Fitzclarence and naturally sought support from their father who, as his influence increased, gave the boys various appointments. Throughout his life, he continued to show affection for this large brood of healthy offspring. Their good health seems to exclude the possibility of his having continued active syphilis.

As time passed, William found himself more and more in debt, eventually deciding that a wealthy wife would settle all his troubles. He wrote to Mrs Jordan, giving her and the many children a suitable settlement, before setting off with his usual enthusiasm, not to say mania, to find a wife. Miss Catherine Tylney, Miss Long, Lady Downshire, Miss Margaret Elphinstone, Lady Berkeley: all received his somewhat unusual advances. All refused him, perhaps repulsed by his blunt manners and speech. Finally he had a brainwave – he would marry the Duchess of Oldenburg, the 25-year-old sister of the Russian Tsar, all his troubles would be settled. The duchess visited England, but found him vulgar and refused the honour.

Matters were to alter in 1817, with the death during childbirth of Charlotte, the only daughter of George, Prince of Wales. This now made William a possible successor to the throne, since his other brother Frederick, Duke of York, had no children. William now pursued a wealthy and eccentric lady, Mrs Wyckham, until his brother, the regent, refused to accept a marriage. William was advised to consider the Princess Adelaide of Saxe-Meiningen, a small and unimportant state. This he did with some reluctance. However, when he met Adelaide they both found each other to their liking, and a very happy marriage was to follow.

In 1818, they were in Hanover when she became pregnant. All seemed to be very happy until Adelaide developed pleurisy and her doctors decided to treat her, with what was possibly the very worst of treatments. Pregnant women are very apt to develop anaemia, and Adelaide's doctors now decided that bleeding would be of benefit, proceeding to bleed her on several occasions. Possibly as a consequence she had a premature birth of a baby daughter, who lived for only a few days. The small child was buried with George I. In 1819, Adelaide again became pregnant and it was decided that she should have this child in England. The journey seemed to upset her and she had a miscarriage at Calais.

In 1820, George III died and was succeeded by the Prince Regent, who seemed unlikely to have children. Adelaide again became pregnant and this time she gave birth to a fine daughter, who was christened Elizabeth. She was a fit little girl, but unfortunately, she developed gastro-enteritis, a common enough complaint of the times. Since she had been breast-fed, it is difficult to see where her infection came from. The fine little girl died, to the great sorrow of her parents. In 1822, again, Adelaide was pregnant, but miscarried twins. If they had lived, they would have been the only children in history to be twin heirs to the throne. William said of his wife, 'I want words to express my feelings at the repeated misfortunes to this beloved and superior woman.'

It does not appear that the miscarriages were due to William having syphilis or any other disease. There was a reasonable explanation in each case for what happened.

In 1827, Frederick, Duke of York, contracted lobar pneumonia from which he died, leaving no children. The favourite child of George III, being somewhat austere and free from the excesses of his elder brother, he had not got on very well with William, who now found himself heir to the throne.

At this point, he was appointed Lord High Admiral, a post which he was very pleased to find was ill defined, nobody knowing precisely what such a person was supposed to do. The last person to have been so appointed was the husband of Queen Anne. Ministers hoped that he would play no active part in naval affairs, but they had not reckoned with William's active personality. He went to sea in his yacht and ordered the squadron that was stationed at Portsmouth to follow. This included capital ships which all had to sail out after William, although it seems that he was not sure where to go. Indeed, he returned to port with no real explanation of his intention. Such behaviour led to rumours that he was showing evidence of the trouble which had afflicted his father.

On 26 June 1830 William was awakened by Sir Henry Halford, who met him buttoning on his trousers. He told him of his brother's death and that he was now King. William promptly returned to bed, 'having never yet slept with a Queen'. As King he showed marked geniality and good humour, perhaps to an excessive degree. It is reported that he once wandered off down St James's and was surrounded by a crowd, having to be rescued by the members of White's Club. He would ride in his coach through the park and lean out from side to side, raising his hat. Was his euphoria natural or due to cerebral abnormality? At his coronation, which he wished to be simple, he lost patience after some two hours in Westminster Abbey and left the church during an anthem. Adept as an after-dinner speaker, he would rise and speak, often for a considerable time and sometimes in a rambling manner; occasionally he would recount naval humour not suitable for the gathering. Attending the opera, he would often fall asleep.

In spite of these eccentricities, William worked very hard at matters of state. His brother had left some 48,000 unsigned documents and had done little work for several years. William set to work to attend to these matters and his ministers had no reason to complain. During his reign, the controversial Reform Bill extending the franchise was passed. He became very popular and changed the public image of monarchy, which meant that his niece, Victoria, started her reign with a great advantage.

By 1836, William started to lose his vitality. He tended to have attacks of temper and it was noted that 'he had shrunk both in mind and body'. After his dinner, he would sleep and then wake, shaking. He was also not so sure on his legs. He had the greatest support from his faithful Adelaide and from one of his daughters, Lady de L'Isle. In 1837, shortly before his own death, his daughter died following childbirth. Nor was his dear wife Adelaide well. William started once again to have attacks of asthma, but on this occasion it is probable that the attacks were cardiac asthma, arising from the onset of cardiac failure.

In May he suffered a collapse and soon needed to have a wheel-chair, due to the shortness of his breath. He could not attend Ascot, as he had always done. He took consolation in religion and had passages of the *Book of Common Prayer* and the Bible read to him. When Waterloo Day came, 18 June, he asked that the great occasion be celebrated as usual, although he could take no part. All his children were now with him, except for his son, Munster. William was dying of cardiac failure and like so many old persons at this time, he developed terminal bronchopneumonia. The shortness of his breath became more severe and at 12 minutes past two, on 20 June 1837, he died.

Although signed by Edward Duke Moore as Apothecary to the Queen, the following report was most probably the work of Sir Astley Cooper, who also signed it. From *The Post-Mortem Examination of his Late Majesty*, made at Windsor Castle on 20 June 1837:

On examining the mortal remains of his late Majesty, William the Fourth, the following appearances were noticed;

In the right cavity of the chest there was an effusion of about 14 ounces of serious fluid.

The lung on that side was nowhere adherent, the vessels of the lower lobe were very much tinged with blood, and the air cells contained a mucous and serious fluid having a bloody tinge.

The left lung adhered generally, and with great firmness, to the surface of the pleura lining the chest; these adhesions appear to have resulted from former attacks of inflammation. The vessels of this lung were also tinged with blood, and its lower portion was somewhat indurated.

The rings of the trachea and bronchi were ossified to a great extent; and the lining membrane was of a dark colour, in consequence of the distended state of the vessels.

The pericardium adhered universally to the surface of the heart, but these adhesions were slight, and appeared to be of very recent formation.

The heart itself was large, and softened in its texture. Its right side was extremely distended with blood, but exhibited no marks of organic disease.

On the left side of the heart, the mitral valves were found to be ossified, and the three semilunar valves of the aorta were in the same state. The ossification was in two of them to such an extent that it must have materially interfered with their function.

The coats of the aorta were much thickened, and on its inner or lining membrane there were several deposits of earthy matter.

The liver was somewhat enlarged and hardened, and was of a granular structure throughout.

The gall-bladder was extremely contracted and contained but little bile.

The spleen was increased to double its normal size and a large portion of its surface was covered with a cartilaginous deposit.

The pancreas was enlarged and indurated.

The stomach and intestines were healthy, except at one part of the large intestine, which was narrowed by a thickening in its inner membrane.

The right kidney was quite sound, but the left was unusually vascular and exhibited a granular appearance. The investing membrane adhered very slightly to it.

The bladder was in a healthy state.

Signed by the above medical men and also by some four others.

We thus see that the immediate cause of death was the condition of the lungs, which showed basal pneumonia. The heart was grossly abnormal with mitral and aortic valvular disease, for which the heart muscle had partially compensated by enlargement. The changes in these valves and in the aorta itself would be of old syphilitic origin. The liver showed cirrhosis and the kidneys chronic granular changes indicating a longstanding disease. The thickening in the large intestine does not appear to have been so severe as to cause an obstruction. It is not described in any detail and could therefore be of either inflammatory or malignant origin. Inflammatory conditions such as a regional colitis could cause thickening and some stenosis. Malignant disease would cause a progressive narrowing of the bowel and lead to a complete obstruction. Neither condition had fully developed at the time of death. Unfortunately, we have no report on the condition of the brain, but as the reports of these times were simple observations with no microscopical examination, such a report might anyway have been of little value. William died of progressive cardiac failure, terminating in pneumonia. He seems to have been very lucky in escaping the overenergetic attentions of the medical men of the day.

Following William's death, there was an outcry against the bulletins which had been issued each day concerning the King. Many medical men felt that they did not bear any relation to the truth, and brought discredit to the profession. They had been wildly optimistic and did not say that he was gravely ill until just before he died. The following are extracts from some of these bulletins:

> Windsor Castle, June 9th: 'The King has suffered for some time from an affection of the chest, which confines His Majesty to his apartment, and has produced considerable weakness, but has not interrupted his usual attention to business.'

> June 15th: 'His Majesty has had a good night, and is in some respects more comfortable this morning.'

> June 18th: 'The symptoms of the King's disease have not increased, but His Majesty is more feeble today.'

> June 19th: 'The King continues in a very weak and feeble state, notwithstanding His Majesty had some quiet sleep in the night. After transacting in his usual business His Majesty received the sacrament from the Archbishop of Canterbury with attention and great apparent comfort.'

> June 20th: 'It has pleased Almighty God to release from his sufferings our most excellent and gracious Sovereign King William IV. His Majesty expired at 12 minutes past 2 o'clock this day.'

Probably these reports were so phrased for a political reason.

Victoria

~

Born Kensington Palace, 19 May 1819
Died Osborne House, 22 January 1901

THE MEDICAL HISTORY of Queen Victoria differs from that of the previous monarchs, in that during her reign medicine was being placed on a scientific footing. Indeed, in the period between Victoria's birth and her accession in 1837, medicine had already taken a considerable step forward. A post-mortem examination was performed on William IV by doctors who gave a very reasonable account of his medical conditions, although they omitted to examine the brain.

Study of the structure of the human body was difficult or impossible, since the law did not allow such study to take place. In the last years of the eighteenth century, medical men obtained bodies for study in a number of ways, all illegal. We can appreciate this difficulty when we consider an incident which took place in Liverpool as late as 1826. Three casks, labelled 'Bitter Salts', were taken down to the quays by a carter. Addressed to a G. Irson of Edinburgh, these were to be shipped in the vessel *Latona*. The casks gave out such a stench that they were opened by the police and were found to contain 11 pickled and salted bodies. The casks had been collected from a cellar under the house of a certain Revd McGowan, and here the police found 19 other bodies, also prepared for transportation. The bodies had been injected for preservation for anatomical purposes. It transpired that these bodies had been taken from the cemetery attached to the Liverpool workhouse by two men, McGregor and Ross, and were being sent to Scotland where bodies fetched £6–£12 each. The men were tried and imprisoned.

This incident was, however, eclipsed in 1828 by the activities of Burke and Hare, in London. The two men had been intoxicating victims and then suffocating them with a view to selling the bodies for anatomical purposes. It was established that 33 murders of this type had taken place. These, and other incidents, caused the government to pass the Anatomy Act in 1838, which governed, and still governs, the dissection and study of the human body for medical purposes.

Victoria was born on 19 May 1819, in Kensington Palace. She was the daughter of the Duke of Kent, the fourth son of George III. Desperately short of money, the duke married the widowed Victoria of Saxe-Coburg. Although he had a permanent mistress, a certain Madame de St Laurent, he also needed money, while the widow needed a husband. The duke and his wife started married life in Germany, but he decided that his child should be born in England. He brought with him a famous midwife, Fräulein Siebold, to attend his wife. She was unique in being both a qualified doctor and a midwife. Perhaps because the duchess had had a previous child by her first marriage, the birth took place with little difficulty and so Victoria, a healthy young girl, was born.

The birth of Victoria had great importance. The only child of George IV, Charlotte, had tragically died in childbirth. This left a vacuum, as George IV had quarrelled with his wife and the couple were most unlikely to have any further children. The Duke of Clarence, the next in line, had no children who survived infancy. His brothers also had no legitimate children, so a race began to produce an heir to the throne. The race was won by the Duke of Kent with the birth of his daughter, Victoria.

The infant Victoria was fortunate in that her mother decided to breastfeed and have her vaccinated for smallpox, which was a very new idea indeed. Edward Jenner was an English physician who lived in Berkeley, Gloucestershire. Here, there was a strong local belief that dairymaids who had cowpox did not catch smallpox, a fairly common endemic disease at this time. This led Jenner to the idea of deliberately infecting people with cowpox in order to prevent them from the more serious condition of smallpox. His ideas of vaccination were to lead to the disappearance of smallpox. Vaccination did not bother the infant Victoria to any great degree and she was in excellent health on 24 June 1819, when she was christened.

Unfortunately, George IV had been chosen as one of the godparents. He insisted that she be called Alexandrina after another godfather, the Tsar of Russia. The name Victoria did not seem to be popular with anyone except her uncle, William, who as a good sailor thought that she was being christened with a name to commemorate Nelson's flagship.

Victoria, known as Drina in her early life, was to hear nothing but German in her first years and it was only after the age of three that she spoke English. Her mother kept her under the strictest control, hardly letting her out of her sight. This isolation kept Victoria away from contact with other children, and so she escaped the childhood diseases so common at the time. Measles, diphtheria, and whooping cough were all avoided, and her childhood progressed with little trouble. It is said that her mother placed a sprig of holly under the child's chin to ensure that she carried her head well.

Although Victoria was fortunate in her health, her father was not. The family were advised to take a holiday in Devon when Victoria was only six months old. Owing to financial stringency, they decided to go to Sidmouth to stay at Weymouth Cottage. Her father caught a cold while visiting Salisbury Cathedral on the journey down to Devon. The cold progressed into a severe chest infection, and the duke contracted pneumonia, from which he died in January 1820, leaving his family in considerable financial difficulty. His wife, the Duchess of Kent, developed a close relationship with Sir John Conroy after her husband's death, and he acted as if he were Victoria's father. Victoria resented Conroy and dismissed him from her court when she became Queen.

Victoria continued in good health until 1835, when on 5 October she felt very ill indeed. This was a rare occurrence and by 7 October, it was obvious that she was seriously ill. She was looked after by her nurse, Lehzen, and a Dr Clark. It appears that she had typhoid, although the diagnosis was often given at this time for cases of gastrointestinal upset with associated fever. Whether Victoria suffered a true attack of typhoid or not is unclear. She was treated with quinine for her fever and given soup and fluids, which would prevent any dehydration. She slowly recovered. By the end of the month she was able to walk a few steps and to take more varied food. She had lost considerable weight and her nurse had to cut her hair short to hide how thin it had become; previously it had been very thick and dark. After five weeks she was able to come downstairs, but it was not until February that she could resume her normal routine. This illness was one of the very few occasions to interrupt Victoria's life.

Two more years were to pass before Victoria was to become Queen. This early part of her life was somewhat unhappy under the strict care of her mother and the detested Sir John Conroy. If her uncle, William IV, had died before she was 18 years old, then her mother would have become Regent. Fortunately William lived for 27 days after her eighteenth birthday, so on his death, in June 1837, Victoria became Queen. The Lord Chamberlain, Archbishop Howley, and the King's physician rode to Kensington to greet her as queen.

In the first few months of her reign she showed a quiet self-confidence. Her health was excellent and from her journals it is clear that she had great affection for her prime minister, Lord Melbourne. She dismissed Sir John Conroy from court, but by 1838 she was involved in constant squabbles with her family and we find her health altering. She became very worried, as her weight had considerably increased and was now 8 stone 13 pounds, in spite of her dieting. She developed a lethargy, finding difficulty in getting up in the morning and a dislike for washing, dressing and undressing. She feared lest she should become like her ancestor George III. Her hands and feet were always cold. She felt that her appearance had become less attractive, that her hair and eyebrows had altered. All these matters would point to an endocrine upset, a condition in which her glands were not functioning correctly. So far as we know her periods continued regularly. Her temper became increasingly short and she was said to have had 'a devil of a temper'.

Her difficulties were increased by an unfortunate event in relation to one of her ladies-in-waiting, Lady Flora Hastings. Victoria saw her getting into a coach with Sir John Conroy and shortly afterwards the Queen noticed that Lady Hastings appeared to be pregnant. No doubt hoping to damage Conroy, Victoria accused Lady

Hastings, who protested her innocence and asserted that she was a virgin. Victoria insisted that she be examined by one of her own doctors; he found that Lady Hastings was indeed a virgin and that her increased size was due to a liver tumour from which the unfortunate lady then died. Details of this event were leaked to the press and did great damage to Victoria's popularity.

Victoria's health always responded to events and it was evident that she needed a new interest in life. The need for a marriage to ensure the succession to the throne was to provide her with a totally new lifestyle and restore her naturally good health. She had a great affection for William Lamb, Viscount Melbourne, and some thought she might marry him. Various dukes and earls from overseas and home also arrived to pay their respects. However, Prince Leopold, husband to the ill-fated Charlotte, had always hoped that Victoria would marry one of the House of Coburg and for some time he had advanced his two nephews, Ernest and Albert, as possible husbands. A visit from Ernest and Albert convinced Victoria that Albert was her favourite.

Albert had not been in good health as a child. His nose bled, his chest was weak and he had attacks of croup. He tired very easily and would fall asleep, even while taking his meals. He always admitted that he had a 'weak stomach'. As he grew up, his health improved and by the time he met Victoria, at the age of 18, he was a very good-looking young man. He is always pictured as tall and thin, but photographs show that he was only about 5 feet 6 inches tall, not much taller than Victoria. Although he was fond of music he was not a very popular youth; strict in his lifestyle, he was a non-drinker and non-smoker, and also unable to mix easily with other men and positively afraid of women. Victoria, however, was charmed by him and they married in February 1840.

They honeymooned at Windsor, where Victoria's journal reveals that she was delighted with Albert and the joys of married life. She had planned to have a few years of married life before having any children, yet seems to have taken no contraceptive precautions. She became pregnant almost immediately and her first child was a girl. The delivery was not easy, taking some 12 hours, but Victoria was a strong young woman of 21 and she recovered very rapidly. Vicky was fed by a wet nurse and Victoria soon returned to normal menstruation and the possibility of further children. She had not long to wait and was pregnant again in 1841. Frequent squabbles with Albert and fits of depression were common before her second delivery, which was somewhat easier than her first, and they were both delighted to have a son, Edward, who was created Prince of Wales a month after his birth. Victoria was to have nine children in all, born in the following years: Alice in 1843, Alfred in 1844, Helena in 1846, Louise in 1848, Arthur in 1850, Leopold in 1853 and Beatrice in 1857. As a result of her pregnancies, she put on considerable weight, which contributed to the shape she assumed in later life.

During this period of her life, her doctor was Sir James Clark. Her deliveries up until the birth of Leopold had been reasonable and her recovery rapid. The delivery of Leopold differed from all the previous ones in that an anaesthetic was used. At this time, Sir Humphrey Davy had shown how anaesthesia could be accomplished by the use of nitrous oxide. This was not suitable for the delivery of children, but volatile anaesthetics were now being introduced, particularly in Edinburgh. Chloroform was given to Victoria during the birth of Leopold by Dr Snow of Edinburgh. He used what is known as the open method, in which a cone-shaped cover of gauze is placed over the patient's face and the chloroform dropped in small quantities so it is received mixed with air. This is a reasonably safe method where the toxic effects of the chloroform are avoided. Victoria was very pleased with the relief it gave her and also used the anaesthetic in her final delivery. Meanwhile, a battle raged between those who thought that anaesthesia should be used and those who felt that pain should not be avoided and who quoted from the Bible: 'In sorrow shalt thou bring forth children.' Victoria, however, was a strong supporter of the new method and her example doubtless contributed to the popularity of painless childbirth.

The year 1854 saw Victoria in good health, although Prince Albert had a number of feverish chills. The Queen's good health contrasted with that of the soldiers fighting for her in the Crimean War. They were far from healthy, and there were reports of fever, diarrhoea, nothing but endless salt pork to eat and no vegetables or tobacco. Victoria's response was to pick up her knitting needles and produce scarves and woollens. A certain Florence Nightingale had other ideas: she set to work to produce a nursing service from which the nurses, who were to staff the new voluntary hospitals, were to come. At the end of the war Victoria, with some trepidation, sent for Florence. She charmed the Queen with her gentle and ladylike manner. Nightingale nurses were to form a select band who greatly increased the standing of the nursing profession. Previously, nurses had often been of poor character. Hospitals were now arising in many provincial cities and the long-established London hospitals were to be staffed by a new professional nursing service. The Voluntary Hospital Service was to expand during Victoria's reign to become one of the greatest services of all time. Nursing reached a peak which was never again equalled. Miss Nightingale also co-operated with architects, such as Waterhouse, to produce excellent hospital buildings which functioned satisfactorily until the onset of the State Medical Service.

Victoria's health was always intimately connected with the happenings of her reign. When all went well she was happy and good-tempered, with no medical complaints. When political trouble stirred she became quarrelsome and was most difficult to please. Following the marriage of her eldest daughter to Frederick of Prussia, both she and Albert became depressed and ill. The Queen showed petulance, obstinacy and bitterness. In spite of this her physical health remained good, in contrast to that of her husband who was a greying, tired man.

Eighteen sixty-one was the year of change. Albert, weak and disillusioned, seemed fast to be losing the will to live. His popularity had sunk to a very low level, particularly with the aristocracy, where his position as a foreigner was never forgotten. In the summer, the royal family visited Ireland, where the Prince of Wales was in camp with the Guards. Victoria and Albert travelled to Killarney, which they considered to be one of the loveliest of places. On the return, the royal yacht crossed to Holyhead and Albert made an excursion to Snowdonia and Llanberis. He seemed to be becoming much fitter and healthier. The couple then returned to Windsor and immediately all their troubles came back: two of Albert's Coburg cousins died of typhoid and a rumour spread throughout Europe that the Prince of Wales was having a love affair with Nellie Clifden. Albert, with his high sense of morality, was deeply shocked. His previous unhealthy state returned, and he suffered sleeplessness, coughing and neuralgia.

Albert then made a visit to Sandhurst, where he was drenched in the rain, before travelling to Cambridge to remonstrate with the Prince of Wales about his behaviour. He now developed a fever he had always dreaded, but instead of taking reasonable precautions and resting he continued with his duties, walking with the Queen to please her. It appears that he had a chest infection for some time before he became seriously ill. The possibility of his having tuberculosis must be considered; tuberculosis and typhoid are often difficult to differentiate. Albert became bedridden, but he still tried to drag himself from his bed to a chair. His doctors were optimistic and reassured the Queen, who did not appear to recognise the real danger for some time. Despite the efforts of his doctors, Albert's condition worsened and he passed away quietly on the night of 14 December 1861. The official diagnosis was that he had died from typhoid.

Following the death of Albert, Victoria fell into a long period of profound mourning. Once before, when her mother had died, she had been so affected that it was thought she might become deranged, and after the death of Albert there were again fears for her sanity. The Queen withdrew almost completely from public life. In the first year of her reign, Parliament had voted to give her £375,000 each year of her life. There were now strong protests and even accusations that she was salting money away. Calls for her son, the Prince of Wales, to take over were common. However, it would appear that her mental health was quite good and her physical state excellent, interrupted by only one serious illness in 1870.

On 4 August she awoke to find that she had been stung on the right elbow, which was causing her pain and steadily swelling. This served as an explanation, once again, of why she could not undertake public appearances. She travelled to Balmoral in spite of having developed a sore throat, which gave her difficulty in swallowing. What seems to have happened is that she developed cellulitis of the arm following her sting. Infections of this type could become very serious indeed with the possibility of septicaemia, in which the infection invades the bloodstream, and before modern antibiotics would have caused death. Dr Jenner, her physician, realised her condition and asked for the help of the distinguished surgeon Professor Lister. Lister prepared her for operative drainage of the abscess using a carbolic acid spray which he had developed himself, to prevent further infection. (This method of preventing infection was used for a time before the idea of boiling all instruments was adopted.) Victoria had been lucky once again, although she had lost some two stone in weight during the illness. She was to be further tried when in November Edward, the Prince of Wales, developed typhoid. He became seriously ill and Victoria had to watch him from behind a screen to avoid infection, although as she had had an attack during her youth she was probably immune anyway. Edward passed through the usual stages of typhoid, with a crisis followed by recovery.

Although Victoria's medical history shows her to be very free from disease, she was constantly troubled by the fear of injury. When she was very young, a boy who was shooting at birds peppered her window with shot. The glass was smashed and some of it tore her gown. When she was 15 her carriage overturned, fortunately not injuring her, although there was considerable danger from the kicking of the fallen horses. Victoria rescued her little dog, then took cover behind a wall. Help was at hand from a Mr Micklethwaite, who restrained a horse by sitting on its head. He was to be made a baronet in the Coronation Honours.

On 10 June 1840, while the Queen was driving with the Prince Consort on Constitution Hill, a youth named Edward Oxford fired twice with pistols from the park side. His bullets were embedded in the wall opposite. He was seized by a man on the footpath, a certain Mr Millais, the father of the famous painter. Victoria and Albert rode on, escorted by an excited crowd of those riding in the park. This attempted assassination won the Queen much public sympathy, particularly as she was pregnant at the time. Oxford was committed to a lunatic asylum.

The further attempts on her life, although very alarming at the time, were not a great danger to her. It appears that most were made by deranged persons without specific motives. The attempts did incidentally boost the popularity both of Albert and of herself. In 1842 there were two further attempts on her life. While driving in The Mall on 30 May, Albert noticed a man pointing a pistol, which must have misfired before he slipped away in the crowd. The following day, Victoria rode again on her usual route, this time with equerries very close to her carriage. The man, John Francis,

appeared once again and fired from about five paces. He was condemned to death, but reprieved when it was proved that his pistol
was not loaded with shot. In July of the same year a small, deformed
boy, John William Been, made a further attempt using a pistol
loaded with paper and tobacco. Despite all these attempts, the couple's greatest trouble at this time was from an attack of influenza
which gave them both considerable trouble. In May 1849, an
Irishman named William Hamilton borrowed his landlady's pistol
and fired at the Queen while she rode on Constitution Hill after her
birthday celebrations. Once again there was no ball in the gun and
no damage done. Hamilton was deported for seven years. There
does not appear to have been any motive for these attacks.

A year later, on 25 July 1850, a somewhat different attack took
place. Victoria was visiting her dying Uncle Adolphus at
Cambridge House and her carriage had to pass through the narrow
entrance gates. The mounted equerries were pushed aside to allow
the carriage to enter, and this allowed the crowd to surge forward
round her carriage. A retired lieutenant of the 10th Hussars named
Pate pushed forward and struck her a severe blow on the head with
his cane. The crowd seized the man, but the Queen calmed the people by staggering to her feet and crying, 'I am not hurt.' Saved by the
strong bonnet she was wearing, she was left with a black eye and
bruises and slight shock. In spite of these injuries, she attended the
opera the same night, receiving a rapturous reception.

In February 1872, a somewhat weak-minded man, Arthur
O'Connor, pointed an unloaded pistol at the Queen in an attempt
to frighten her so that Fenian prisoners might be released. Prince
Arthur attempted to leap on the man but was too slow, as her trust-
ed servant John Brown had already seized him. The Queen showed
her thanks to Brown by awarding him a gold medal and an annuity
of £25. O'Connor was sentenced to one year's imprisonment, but
the Queen feared that he might attack again more seriously and
requested that he be deported. O'Connor agreed to go abroad vol-
untarily.

March 1882 saw the last attempt on her life, when Roderick
McLean fired at her carriage while it was outside Windsor station.
Two boys from Eton College belaboured the man with their
umbrellas. Once again, McLean proved to be an imbecile. Apart
from the assurance Victoria felt from having John Brown with her,

she also received increased protection from outriders. It was now suggested that she be provided with a parasol lined with mail, which could be used as a protection. It was made for her, but proved to be so heavy, with its plated lining, that it was impractical for use. It is still to be seen in the London Museum.

In later life, Victoria became more and more removed from her public role. She developed a great liking for Balmoral, more particularly when she came under the influence of John Brown, who undoubtedly did much to maintain her health. He encouraged rides and walks, which served to prevent Victoria becoming progressively immobile. We read in her journal that she suffered from many minor ailments, including rheumatism, gout and neuralgia. These were all greatly aggravated by a fall down stairs at Windsor on 17 March 1883. She was confined to a sofa for a week and became vexed because Brown was unable to attend her, having himself become seriously ill. Brown was attended by the Queen's doctors Dr Reid and Sir William Jenner. With the death of Brown in 1883 she lost the impetus to take exercise and became much heavier. We are able to get some idea of her physical state from her clothing, which is preserved. Her waist measurement was 46 inches and it would appear that she lost several inches in height, a condition not unusual in old age. As she had been only 5 feet 2 inches tall in her youth, she must have been very small indeed.

By the time of her diamond jubilee in 1897, Victoria was not able to walk into St Paul's owing to her 'lameness'. Nevertheless, she did appear once again in public when she made an historic progress through London to celebrate the jubilee on 22 June 1897, receiving possibly the greatest reception ever given to a reigning monarch. She recorded the great event in her journal with much pride. But Victoria also started losing many friends at this time, as both her personal maid and Mr Gladstone died.

In her last years Victoria suffered from increasing insomnia, although she was very apt to fall asleep during the day. Her ladies had been able to keep her awake when in her carriage by repeatedly rearranging her cushions. She became very irritable and had some loss of memory, although she still wrote her journal daily. At Osborne she fell into a routine of going to bed at 10 p.m., but chloral and Bengers food failed to give her much sleep. She was not therefore really awake until noon and so much of the day was wasted. The year 1900 was a trying one for her with the monotonous routine of sleepless nights and tiring days. In January 1901 she had some reasonable days and on the 11th she was able to go out. Two days later comes a stop to the journal which she had kept for 69 years. We know she was put into her pony chaise on 15 January, but the day was not fine enough for her to go out. By the 17th she was suffering from mental confusion and difficulty with speech; she was passing away, as so many very aged persons do, in a state of confusion, but with no special local cause for death. The Prince of Wales and the Kaiser arrived on the 19th, when the dying Queen asked to have Turi, her little Pomeranian dog, on her lap. The local vicar from Whippingham and Randall Davidson, the Bishop of Winchester, were in attendance. As she lapsed in and out of consciousness, she was supported on one side by the Prince of Wales and on the other by the Kaiser. At 6.30 p.m., surrounded by her children and grandchildren, the aged Queen died. Her strong constitution had carried her through such a long a reign with little illness and brought her to a death at a great age from senile decay.

The children of Victoria were to marry into several of the royal houses of Europe. Leopold, who was born in 1853, suffered from haemophilia. This condition is caused by an abnormal gene carried by the female line, but suffered as a disease by the male descendants. Her daughter, Alice, carried the abnormality into the royal house of Russia, and the son of Tsar Nicholas, murdered by the Communists, suffered from haemophilia. The complexities of heredity are indeed difficult to follow, but it is possible that this abnormal gene came from Victoria's mother, Victoria of Saxe-Coburg.

Appendix I

&

THE PROBABLE CAUSES OF DEATH OF THE
KINGS AND QUEENS OF ENGLAND

WILLIAM I Rupture of the urethra. Extravasation of urine.
Uraemia (kidney failure).

WILLIAM II Murder: arrow wound.

HENRY I Perforated duodenal ulcer. Peritonitis. Paralytic ileus.

STEPHEN Acute appendicitis. Peritonitis.

HENRY II Manic depressive syndrome. Bronchopneumonia.

RICHARD I Septicaemia: arrow wound.

JOHN Perforated peptic ulcer (possibly poisoning).

HENRY III Cerebral haemorrhage (stroke).

EDWARD I Carcinoma (cancer) of the rectum.

EDWARD II Murder: traumatic perforation of the rectum;
peritonitis.

EDWARD III Cerebral thrombosis (right side). Bronchopneumonia.

RICHARD II Poisoning (possibly by amanita).

HENRY IV Chronic nephritis. Uraemia (kidney failure). Chronic
pemphigus (a severe skin condition).

HENRY V Carcinoma (cancer) of the rectum. Bronchopneumonia. Pleurisy.

HENRY VI Murder: multiple stab wounds.

EDWARD IV Bronchopneumonia. Pleurisy. Pleural effusion.

EDWARD V Murder: suffocation.

RICHARD III Killed in battle.

HENRY VII Pulmonary tuberculosis. Renal tuberculosis. Uraemia
(kidney failure).

HENRY VIII Cushing syndrome (abnormality of the glands). Uraemia. Chronic nephritis. Gravitational ulcer of the leg. Amyloid disease.

EDWARD VI Acute pulmonary tuberculosis. Measles.

MARY I Ovarian tumour.

ELIZABETH I Suppurative parotitis (infected parotid gland). Bronchopneumonia. Carcinoma (cancer) of the stomach. Myxoedema (thyroid failure).

JAMES I Bronchopneumona. Pulmonary tuberculosis.

CHARLES I Execution: beheaded.

CROMWELL Pyelonephritis. Vesical stone. Uraemia (kidney failure).

CHARLES II Uraemia (kidney failure). Chronic nephritis. Syphilis.

JAMES II Cerebral thrombosis. Hypertension. Syphilitic vascular disease.

MARY II Acute smallpox.

WILLIAM III Pulmonary embolism (clot). Deep venous thrombosis. Fractured clavicle. Bronchopneumonia.

ANNE Uraemia (kidney failure). Chronic nephritis. Hypochromic anaemia. Lupus erythematosus.

GEORGE I Cerebral haemorrhage (stroke). Hypertension.

GEORGE II Rupture of the ventricle (heart). Syphilitic aortitis.

GEORGE III Bronchopneumonia. Terminal dementia. Porphyria.

GEORGE IV Gastric haemorrhage. Portal hypertension. Hepatic cirrhosis (cirrhosis of the liver). Aortic and mitral valvular disease. Diverticulum of the bladder. Calculus.

WILLIAM IV Bronchopneumonia. Aortic and mitral valvular disease. Myocarditis. Syphilis.

VICTORIA Cardiac failure. Senility.

Appendix II

∾

THE ROYAL TOMBS

EDWARD THE CONFESSOR – died 1066. He established the royal church of Westminster Abbey and this was where his chapel shrine was placed. It became a place of pilgrimage. The shrine was relocated in the abbey by Henry III.

HAROLD – died 1066. The exact burial place is not known, but it is said that he was taken to Waltham Abbey in Essex, where a plain slab was placed.

WILLIAM I – died 1087. He was buried in the Monastery of St Etienne at Caen, where he remained until the sixteenth century, when the tomb was opened. The Calvinists desecrated it and scattered the bones. A new tomb was destroyed in the revolution of 1793. A plain tomb remains, which escaped damage during the heavy fighting of 1944.

WILLIAM II – died 1100. Lies in Winchester Cathedral, possibly in the mortuary chests on the choir screen, but a tomb is to be seen in the main choir at Winchester.

HENRY I – died 1135. His viscera were buried in Rouen where he died. His embalmed body was buried in Reading Abbey. After the dissolution the abbey was used as a quarry and now lies in ruins.

STEPHEN – died 1154. Buried in the Abbey of the Holy Saviour, Faversham. The tomb also contained his queen and his son, but it was later desecrated and destroyed, and the remains lost.

MATILDA – died 1167. She briefly held power from her cousin, Stephen, but left England, having secured the succession for her son. She is buried in Rouen Cathedral.

HENRY II – died 1189. Buried at Fontevrault.

RICHARD I – died 1199. Lies buried penitent at the feet of his father at Fontevrault. His heart was buried in Rouen Cathedral, where a small statue was discovered in 1838 with a lead box containing a silver box. Inside lay the heart 'reduced to the semblance of a dried reddish leaf'.

JOHN – died 1216. Buried in Worcester Cathedral. The tomb was opened in 1797 and the corpse found enclosed in a monk's cowl. A sword and scabbard were also present.

HENRY III – died 1272. Buried in the 'new' Westminster Abbey over the original site of Edward the Confessor's grave. He rebuilt the abbey and removed the Confessor's shrine.

EDWARD I – died 1307. He asked that his body be boiled down and the bones carried by his army into Scotland, while his heart was to go to the Holy Land. The body was actually buried in Westminster Abbey in a black marble tomb.

EDWARD II – died 1327. Murdered in Berkeley Castle, his tomb is in Gloucester Cathedral.

EDWARD III – died 1377. Tomb in Westminster Abbey with his queen.

EDWARD THE BLACK PRINCE – died 1376. Tomb and armour are in Canterbury Cathedral.

RICHARD II – died 1382. He originally lay at Langley, Herefordshire, but was taken to Westminster Abbey by Henry V. The side plates of his tomb were loose for many years and several oddments were pushed through into the tomb. It was possible to touch the skull through the opening in the coffin and in 1776 a schoolboy stole the jaw bone. It was kept in his family until 1906, when it was returned. All the oddments were removed when the tomb was restored in 1880. He married Anne of Bohemia, who died in 1384 and lies in a fine tomb in the abbey.

HENRY IV – died 1413. Lies in Canterbury Cathedral along with his uncle, the Black Prince. The tomb was opened in 1 831 and was found to contain a lead coffin with a leather-wrapped, embalmed corpse with well-preserved features. The body had a reddish beard. His second wife, Joan of Navarre, lies with him.

HENRY V – died 1422. His corpse was returned from France for burial at Westminster and the tomb was surmounted by a magnificent effigy in oak plated with silver. Henry VIII removed the valuable effigy, including the solid silver head. The body of his wife, Catherine de Valois, was placed in a tomb, but removed by Henry VIII and left unburied in the abbey behind the high altar in a plain wooden box. There she remained until 1793 when she was reburied.

HENRY VI – died 1471 . Buried at Chertsey, Surrey, but reinterred in St George's Chapel, Windsor.

EDWARD IV – died 1483. Lies in St George's Chapel, Windsor.

EDWARD V – died 1483. Said to have been murdered in the Tower of London. There is now an urn in Westminster Abbey (near to the tomb of Elizabeth I) which reputedly contains the remains of the two Princes in the Tower, placed here by Charles II in 1678.

RICHARD III – died 1485. His body was originally buried at the Greyfriars Church in Leicester, which has been destroyed. His remains were dug up and are said to have been flung into the River Soar in 1540 at the dissolution of the abbeys. His son has a shrine in the Chapel of St Nicholas, Sheriff Hutton Church, near York.

HENRY VII – died 1509. There is a magnificent shrine in the special Chapel of Henry VII in Westminster Abbey. He lies with his wife, Elizabeth of York, but James I was placed in his tomb and lies between the two. His eldest son, Arthur, predeceased him and is buried in Worcester Cathedral; his second son became Henry VIII.

HENRY VIII – died 1547. Lies in a plain marble tomb in St George's Chapel, Windsor, along with his queen Jane Seymour.

CATHERINE OF ARAGON lies in Peterborough Cathedral.

ANNE BOLEYN lies in St Peter's Chapel, Tower of London. Her heart is said to have been removed.

ANNE OF CLEVES is buried in Westminster Abbey.

CATHERINE HOWARD lies in St Peter's Chapel.

CATHERINE PARR lies in Sudeley Castle, Gloucestershire.

EDWARD VI – died 1553. His tomb is in the Henry VII Chapel, Westminster Abbey.

LADY JANE GREY – died 1554. Lies in St Peter's Chapel, Tower of London.

MARY I – died 1558. She was buried in Westminster Abbey but was reinterred within the shrine of Elizabeth I. Elizabeth is above Mary and it is said that the heavy coffin of Elizabeth is compressing that of Mary.

MARY, QUEEN OF SCOTS – died 1587. Buried in Peterborough Cathedral until 1612 when her son, James I, wished her to have a tomb equal to that of Elizabeth. Accordingly she was re-interred in Westminster Abbey with a very large and fine tomb. It now contains not only the Queen's coffin but also those of her grandson, Henry, Prince of Wales; her granddaughter, Elizabeth of Bohemia; her great-grandson, Prince Rupert of the Rhine; and the royal children who died in infancy: the first ten children of James II and John Darnley, his natural son; 16 babies born to Queen Anne and her sole surviving child, the Duke of Gloucester; and Lady Arabella

Stuart. The tomb was opened and tidied up under the orders of Dean Stanley in 1867. The Queen's coffin was not touched and the little children surrounding her were left in place.

ELIZABETH I – died 1603. Her instructions not to embalm her body were not followed and her heart was placed in the same casket as that of her sister Mary, in Westminster Abbey.

JAMES I – died 1625. After a prolonged lying-in-state at Westminster he was buried at night with little pomp and the body was 'lost' for many years, nobody knowing where the corpse rested. He was 'found' when the tomb of Henry VII was opened.

CHARLES I – died 1649. After his execution his body was placed in the vault of the tomb of Henry VIII in St George's Chapel, Windsor. This tomb was opened in the presence of George IV in 1813. On reclosing the tomb it was found that a bone, the fourth cervical vertebra, had not been reburied, but had been retained by Sir Henry Halford, one of the royal surgeons doing the inspection. The small bone was used as a salt cellar until Queen Victoria had it returned. It was placed in a small box and returned to the coffin.

CHARLES II – died 1685. Buried in the Chapel of Henry VII, Westminster Abbey, beneath a simple inscribed stone. His wax effigy remains.

JAMES II – died 1701. Died in Paris and buried at St Germain.

MARY II – died 1694 and WILLIAM III – died 1702. Both lie in a simple vault in Westminster Abbey, their wax effigies remaining.

ANNE – died 1714. She and her husband are buried in the Chapel of Henry VII in Westminster Abbey. Seventeen of her infants are in the tomb of Mary, Queen of Scots.

GEORGE I – died 1727. Buried in Leineschloss Church, Hanover, which was severely damaged in World War II. After it was rebuilt, his remains were removed to a mausoleum in the Herrenhausen Gardens.

GEORGE II – died 1760. He and his wife, Caroline of Ansbach, share a vault in the Chapel of Henry VII. He is the last king to be buried in Westminster Abbey. His son, Frederick Louis, who was the father of George III, is also buried in the chapel.

GEORGE III – died 1820. He and his wife Charlotte are buried in St George's Chapel, Windsor.

GEORGE IV – died 1830. Buried in St George's Chapel, Windsor.

WILLIAM IV – died 1837. Buried in St George's Chapel, Windsor.

VICTORIA – died 1901. Buried in the Royal Mausoleum, Frogmore, Windsor.

Appendix III

❦

SELECT BIBLIOGRAPHY TO MATTERS OF MEDICAL INTEREST

ANON. *Life of William III.* 1706.

ANON. *History of Life and Bloody Reign and Death of Queen Mary.* London, 1682.

ANON. 'Head of Charles I'. *British Medical Journal* 1; 209. 1906.

ANON. 'Some Royal Death Beds'. *British Medical Journal* 1303–1304. 1910.

ANON. 'The Last Illness and Post Mortem of Charles 1st'. *University College Hospital Magazine* 19; 18–24, 61–67. London, 1934.

APPLEBY, L.H. 'The Medical Life of Henry'. *Bulletin of Vancouver Medical Association* 10; 87–101.

AYLING, S.E. *The Georgian Century.* George G. Harrap, Sydney.

BINGHAM, Caroline. *The Life and Times of Edward II.* Weidenfeld & Nicolson, London.

BOWLE, J. *Charles I.* Weidenfeld & Nicolson, London, 1975.

BROWN, M.W. 'Tragedy of Dr Lopez'. *Medical Journal of Red* 133; 609–10.

BRUCE, Marie Louise. *The Usurper King.* Rubicon Press, London.

BRYANT, Arthur. *The Age of Chivalry.* Collins, London, 1963.

BRYANT, Arthur. *The Fire and the Rose.* Collins, London, 1965.

CHANCELLOR, John. *Edward I.* Weidenfeld & Nicolson, London.

CHEVERS, N. 'Did James Die from the Effects of Poison?'. *Ind Annals Medical Society* 15; 187–252, 1.

CHURCHILL, Winston S. *History of the English-speaking Peoples.* Cassell, London, 1956.

CLEMENS, J.R. 'Notes of English Medicine, Henry VIII–George IV'. *Annals of Medical History* 3; 308–17.

CLARK, Sir George, series ed. *Oxford History of England.* Oxford University Press, Oxford.

CLARKE, J.S. *Life of James II* Vol. 2. London, 1816.

COOPER, A.P. 'The Official Report of the Morbid Appearances which Were Observed at the Post-mortem Examination of the Body of His Late Majesty George the Fourth'. *Lancet* 2; 550–1. 1830.

CURTIS, G. *Queen Anne.* Weidenfeld & Nicolson, London, 1972.

DELEIB, E. *Silver Boxes.* Herbert Jenkins, London, 1968.

DILKLER, T. 'Insanity of George III'. *Transactions of the American Neurological Association* 67; 229. 1941.

DORAN, C.H. *Medical History Essays.* New York.

DUFF, D. *Albert and Victoria.* Frederick Muller, London, 1972.

DULKEN, H.W. *History of England.* Lock & Co, London, 1888.

EARLE, P. *James II.* Weidenfeld & Nicolson, London, 1972.

EMSON, H.E. 'The Obstetric History of Queen Anne'. *British Medical Journal* Vol. 304, no 6838; 1365–6. 1992.

FOY, G. 'An Historical Autopsy'. *Janus* 1; 572–3. 1896.

FLUGEL, J.C. 'On the Character and Married Life of Henry VIII'. *International Journal of Psychology* 1; 24–5. 1920.

FRANCIS, W. 'George III'. *British Medical Journal* 1. 213–4. 1914.

FRASER, Antonia. *Cromwell.* Weidenfeld & Nicolson, London, 1973.

FRENCH, Charles C. *George III.* Allen Lane, London, 1975.

GEIKIE-COBB. *The Glands of Destiny.* Heinemann Press, London, 1947.

GILLINGHAM, J. *Richard I.* Weidenfeld & Nicolson, London, 1973.

GOODHALL, A.L. 'The Health of James VI of Scotland'. *Medical History London* 1; 17–27. 1957.

HALFORD, Sir Henry. *Essays and Orations at the Royal College of Physicians.* London, 1831.

HALTON, R. *George I.* Thames & Hudson, London, 1978.

HIBBERT, C. *Charles I.* Weidenfeld & Nicolson, London, 1986.

JAMES, R.R. 'The Medical History of William the Conqueror'. *Lancet* 1; 1151. 1937.

JOHNSON, C. *Elizabeth Tudor, the Lonely Queen.* London, 1954.

JOHNSON, C. 'A Royal Consumptive'. *British Chest Journal* 53; 369–71. 1959.

JOHNSON, P. *The Life and Times of Edward III.* Weidenfeld & Nicolson, London, 1973.

KENDALL, Paul Murray. *Richard III.* Unwin Hyman, London, 1975.

LABARGE, M.W. *Henry V.* Secker & Warburg, London, 1975.

LONGFORD, Elizabeth. *The Oxford Book of Royal Anecdotes.* Oxford University Press, Oxford, 1989.

LONGFORD, Elizabeth. *Victoria R.I.* Weidenfeld & Nicolson, London, 1964.

MacALPINE, Ida & HUNTER, Richard. *George III and the Mad Business.* Allen Lane, London, 1969.

MACLAURIN, C. *Mere Mortals.* 1925.

MacNALTY, Sir A.S. *The Princes in the Tower.* London.

MARSHALL, Dorothy. *Victoria.* Weidenfeld & Nicolson, London, 1972.

MITCHELL. *History Today* Vol. 16, no 2; 149–56. 1966.

MORLEY, John. *Oliver Cromwell.* Macmillan & Co, London, 1900.

NICHOLLS, F. 'Observations Concerning the Body of His Late Majesty'. *Transactions of the Royal Philosophical Society London* 11; 574–9.

NORMAN, H.J. 'The Relation of Mental Disorder to Events in History'. *Bulletin of the Medical Libraries Association* 33; 67–79. 1945.

P.S. 'Why Queen Elizabeth Never Married'. *Urol Review* 31; 399. 1927.

PACKARD, F.R. 'Sir Henry Halford's Account of the Opening of the Tomb of Charles I'. *Annals of Medical History* 3; 196–8.

RAE, J. *Deaths of the Kings of England.* Sherratt & Hughes, London, 1912.

ROSS, C. *Edward IV.* Redwood Burn Ltd, London, 1975.

SATRE, A. 'Les mésaventures d'un cadavre'. *Paris Medical Supplement;* 360–2. 1948.

STOW, John. *Survey of London.* 1598; many modern editions.

THOMSON, C.J.S. 'Did Henry Die from the Effects of Eating Lampreys?' *Mysteries of History.* Lippincott, Philadelphia, 1928.

THOMSON, C.J.S. 'Was James Poisoned?' *Mysteries of History;* 73–80. Lippincott, Philadelphia, 1928.

TREVELYAN, G.M. *English Social History.* Longmans, Green & Co, 1942.

WALPOLE, G. *George II.* London, 1846.

WEDGWOOD, C.V. *The Trial of Charles I.* London, 1964.

WITHERS P. *Parliament House of Commons. George III and His Mental Illness.* Logographic Press, London.

YEARSLEY, M. *Le Roy est Mort.* Heritage Unicorn Press, London, 1935.

ZEE, H. & B. van der. *William and Mary.* Macmillan, London, 1973.

REFERENCES TO MEDIEVAL WRITINGS ARE TO BE FOUND IN THE FOLLOWING:

Adam of Usk's Chronicle. Angliae ad Maunde Thompson, Rolls Series, 1874.

Anglo Saxon Chronicle. Tr. G.N. Garmonsway. Dent, London, 1943.

Annales Monastici. Ed. H.R. Luard. Rolls Series, London, 1864–69.

Branwell Chronicle. Ed. W. Stubbs. Rolls Series, London, 1872–73.

Gervase of Canterbury. Ed. W. Stubbs. Rolls Series, London, 1876.

Great Chronicle of London. Ed. A.H. Thomas, London, 1938.

Jean Froissart, Chronicle. Ed. K. de Littenlove, Brussels, 1867.

Matthew Paris, Chronica Maiora. Ed. H.R. Luard. Rolls Series, London, 1872–84.

Orderic Vitalis, Historia Ecclesiastica. Ed. A.E. Provist. Société de l'Histoire de France, Paris, 1838.